P9-CDL-159

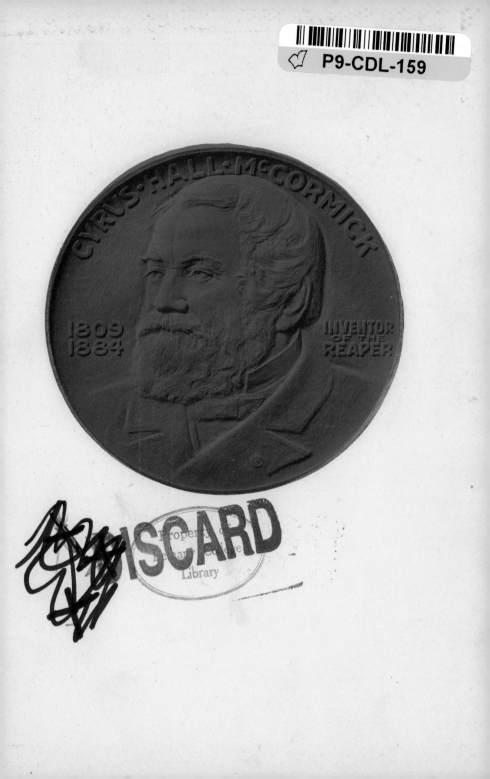

DISCARD

Property of
Library

THE CENTURY OF THE REAPER

CYRUS HALL McCORMICK
Inventor of the Reaper
About 1880

THE CENTURY OF THE REAPER

An *Account* of CYRUS HALL MCCORMICK, the *Inventor* of the *Reaper*: of the MCCORMICK HARVESTING MACHINE COMPANY, the *Business* he created: and of the INTERNATIONAL HARVESTER COMPANY, his *Heir* and chief *Memorial*

BY

CYRUS McCORMICK

With Illustrations

Boston and New York
HOUGHTON MIFFLIN COMPANY
The Riverside Press Cambridge
1931

COPYRIGHT, 1931, BY CYRUS McCORMICK

ALL RIGHTS RESERVED INCLUDING THE RIGHT TO REPRODUCE
THIS BOOK OR PARTS THEREOF IN ANY FORM

The Riverside Press

CAMBRIDGE · MASSACHUSETTS

PRINTED IN THE U.S.A.

TO
MY GRANDMOTHER

P3713

FOREWORD

THIS book represents such honor as I can pay to the life-work of the inventor of the reaper. It must be obvious that I, his grandson, am not in a position to write a coldly impartial account of his contribution to history. I am too proud of his career, and of its continuation in the life-work of other members of my family and their associates, to be anything but a partisan as to Cyrus Hall McCormick's place in the perspective of time. I believe, further, that the countless Harvester men who are following in his footsteps are themselves actuated largely by the pride they feel in their employment. There is something eminently satisfactory in being engaged in a worth-while task.

I hope the account I now give will be accepted, not as propaganda for any special interest, but as a partial record of a century of development in certain phases of the agricultural implement industry. It has not been prepared as an official statement of harvesting machine history inspired in any way by the International Harvester Company. Nevertheless, that organization has a definite place in the picture as the lineal descendant of the business my grandfather founded. I could not have told the story of the events which have led up to the reaper's centennial celebration without indicating that I respect it too. After all, there is no reason why this generation may not take pride in its own sincerity as well as in the fine deeds of its forbears.

Prejudiced though I may be in favor of the reaper and its machine heirs, I have endeavored to be as accurate as possible in the presentation of the facts of this story of a century. While I have gone to original sources as often as possible, the exigencies of my own day-to-day duties in the International Harvester Company have left too little time for original research. I have therefore had recourse to such secondary material as the excellent summary, 'Cyrus Hall McCormick and the Reaper,' by Thwaites; to Casson's two picturesque books, 'Cyrus Hall McCormick' and 'The Romance of the Reaper'; to Ardrey's 'American Agricultural Implements'; and to an unpublished thesis by Leigh, 'Marketing of Harvesting Machinery.'

Most of all I have relied for the facts relating to my grandfather's earlier career on his biographer, Professor William T. Hutchinson, the first volume of whose 'Cyrus Hall McCormick' has just been published by the Century Company, of New York. It is to be regretted that the second volume, which will cover the period from the Civil War to McCormick's death, cannot appear for some time. Until then it will be impossible to get a complete picture of my grandfather's life without a painstaking examination of one of the most voluminous bodies of private and official correspondence I have ever seen.

For the middle period of this century of farm equipment progress, I have leaned heavily upon my father's diaries and upon conversations with him and with Mr. Alexander Legge, whose keen perception has missed little of significance in the most recent forty years of the life of the McCormick Harvesting Machine Company and the International Harvester Company. I have also had the invaluable help of certain business associates whose active careers have spanned the period of my life. Mr. M. J. Rodney, still an active Harvester man in charge of the Company's Australian affairs, has provided me with a store of anecdotes concerning the fine old fighting days. Many other delightful and stimulating stories have come from Mr. H. H. Wiggin and the members of the Harvester Club of Southern California, an organization of retired warriors whose loyalty to Harvester ideals is one of the bright spots in Harvester history. They have collected for me many recollections which deserve far more attention than the small place such a cursory book as this has been able to provide.

Needless to say I have been on surer ground for source material concerning more recent times. I have myself been actively engaged in this business since 1915, either in distribution or production, and I have been in daily association with men whose years of service have been co-extensive with the years of the International Harvester Company. Aside from the memory of my own experiences, I have been greatly helped by references to the files of the *Harvester World*, to the Company's published annual statements, and to the mass of correspondence, speeches on Company policy, articles, etc., which exhibit the progressive growth of a constantly developing business.

Many members of the present Harvester organization have helped me enormously. I wish I might name them all; but it has seemed better to allow the achievements of to-day to remain anonymous. Some have placed at my disposal their own researches into the history of the business. Others have been good enough to read my manuscript, to restrain my exuberance for the subject, and to do all those thankless but friendly tasks which confront the critics of an amateur author. Others have given me pointed, but, I confess, constructive, criticisms on my effort as a writer of history.

But is this history? I like to think of it rather as part of a living drama of I know not how many continuing scenes.

The play tells the story of American industry and this narrative is a part of it. We are the actors of the moment, successors of those actors of the past to whose lives and work we owe our opportunity to serve.

C. McC.

Chicago, *January* 1, 1931

CONTENTS

ILLUSTRATIONS

THE CENTURY OF THE REAPER

THE CENTURY OF
THE REAPER

∴

CHAPTER I

THE INVENTION OF THE REAPER

MODERN agriculture was born in Virginia on a hot July day in 1831. There is no written record of what took place on that momentous occasion. Even the exact date is lost in the maze of unwritten history. But on that afternoon Cyrus Hall McCormick demonstrated to a skeptical but needy world that his work was worthy.

It is hardly to be assumed that the world beyond the Valley of Virginia was excited or eager, or that a huge crowd gathered to witness the trial of the first reaper or to speculate upon its future. Great events are quietly born. Inferentially we may guess that the inventor's parents, his sisters and his young brothers had driven down the Valley from their home. His father, who had spent so many years trying in vain to build a reaper, may have hoped for success for the boy, but he feared that the problem would prove insolvable. His mother stood a little apart, lovingly proud of her tall son whether his reaper worked or not, ready with comfort or praise or renewed encouragement. Jo Anderson was there, the Negro slave who, through the crowded hours of the recent weeks, had helped build the reaper. There were also harvesters, men who had been toiling in the adjacent fields and had laid down their scythes and sickles to come and watch the new-fangled wheat-cutting machine. They knew a better way: they could inch their way through a field of ripe grain, swinging forward in a long line, swinging their heavy blades into the tough stalks while behind them the binders bowed and rose and bowed again. What traffic should they have with a harvesting machine? They and the generations of their fathers before them had learned how to labor with their hands.

Perhaps also there may have been a covered wagon passing, as a much later engraving illustrating the event shows, but if this was not actual, it was at least symbolic. Westward, beyond the sunset, lay the prairies; and those emigrants, who from their wagon thus casually watched the world's first reaper work for the first time, may well have carried away with them word to the empty spaces to prepare for a golden yield of grain. The machine which was to give the prairies the vigor of use was being born.

The reaper marched through the grain. A boy rode the single horse. Jo Anderson walked beside it, rake in hand, to keep the platform clean of severed grain. And behind it strode the young inventor. Tall, square-shouldered, high of brow, purposeful, wise before his time, sensing but not yet seeing the future, determined, feeling the power of destiny within him — Cyrus Hall McCormick paced after his reaper. He turned neither to the right nor left; he was unconscious of the little crowd or the magnificence of his accomplishment. He watched his reaper work.

The hazy hills of Virginia were green with dense woods. Back of them were blue mountain ranges which even now are still the chief beauty of the Valley. To-day that field is almost unrecognizable. A concrete highway passes through it, a gasoline filling station occupies a corner where a side road leads away to Walnut Grove farm, and humming telegraph wires mar the primitive

LITHOGRAPH ISSUED ABOUT 1883 BY THE McCORMICK HARVESTING MACHINE COMPANY, DEPICTING THE FIRST PUBLIC TRIAL OF McCORMICK'S REAPER NEAR STEELE'S TAVERN, VIRGINIA, IN 1831

charm of the landscape. Except for John Steele's Tavern, part of which still stands, the rush of modern times has tried to blot out history; but the fact of accomplishment lives on. As I have stood there, the place has seemed in very truth a field of destiny.

Quietly, unostentatiously, a great deed was passing into actuality. Big things are simple, and those deeds which ring in the consciousness of later generations are too frequently unheralded by the times they call their own. Cyrus Hall McCormick's initial step into history went unnoticed in 1831, but it had been prepared by the subtle planning of unerring destiny.

It would be a fruitless effort to seek to assess the value to the modern world of the great pioneer inventors who, by sheer force of intellect, freed men from toil and gave them hope. Their names are spread upon the annals of half a century. Many of them were so eminent that they would each alone have seemed the crowning genius of an epoch. Their work is most significant when its results are considered in relation to each other and to their times.

Stephenson in England and Fulton in America employed the known principle of steam and made it useful for transportation on land and water. Morse invented the telegraph. McCormick built the reaper and transmuted farming from drudgery into efficiency. Whitney's cotton gin made that volume production of cotton possible which created a world-wide industry. Howe's sewing machine brought women relief from endless toil throughout civilization. Bessemer invented a process and immediately steel became available for all men. And yet we must admit that transportation would have remained a pleasant but unnecessary luxury unless there had been grain and cotton to carry from the country to the city. The reaper would have been purposeless if industry had been unable to absorb the farm labor it released. Machinery in the modern form could not have existed but for steel. In truth, the elements of progress are correlated and interdependent.

Inventions are the product of need. That need may exist simply because people desire something; but it is profounder if there is a sound economic reason for its existence. Behind the great inventors of the first half of the nineteenth century lay the most powerful sanction of economic necessity. This was so to a remarkable degree in the case of the reaper. Before Cyrus Hall McCormick's time, agriculture struggled along with the same means and methods that were in vogue when history dawned. If the rest of civilization could have suddenly become modern while agriculture remained in the slough of inefficiency, the economic results would have been disastrous.

The population of the United States, for example, was about thirteen million in 1831. Three-quarters of these people lived in the country. Sixty years later, when the population had risen to sixty-three million, over half of the people lived in the cities, and nearly twenty million people had been assimilated into urban life who, but for the reaper and its heirs, would have been absolutely required on the farms to produce food for the multitude. Industry was able to claim its share of them and to give them productive jobs. What if the need of the farms for labor had withheld them? Machine industry could not have existed; our Nation's industrial prosperity would have died unborn; we could never have become strong and rich and materially triumphant. Farming is our basic industry, and, had there been a clash of interest between the cities and the country, the former would have had to be served. Men must eat; but to do so they would have had to forgo the benefits of industry if there had been no reaper.

As a matter of fact, agriculture had hardly been able during all its history to keep abreast of the demands of an increasing world population for food. Very recently we have seen how disaster could overwhelm Russia when the balance of agriculture was dislocated. In 1921, Russian farms were practically devoid of agricultural equipment. Farming had returned to the epoch of the mattock and the hoe. There arose differences between the interests of the cities and the country. The peasants stopped producing food, even for themselves. People were starving by millions. In our own times famine stalks through a land as soon as food production fails.

Such things can happen all too easily, even without the confusion of political controversy. There was widespread famine in Europe as late as 1816. There were bread riots in New York in 1837. Before the development of transportation, a locality which suffered from bad weather at the time of harvest would almost certainly face famine before the next winter was over: starving peasants might emigrate to another district if they had strength to escape, but, when their own fields failed them, they could not bring in their bread. The plagues of Egypt are a Biblical record of adverse climatic conditions and insufficient crops. Man can live without comforts and clothes and houses, can even continue a sort of existence without happiness — but he must have food. Always until the advent of farm machinery the problem of food meant the wretchedness of dreary toil and the despair of uncertainty and fear.

Population and famine are matters which affect the many, whereas labor bears directly on the individual who experiences it. Labor is not disheartening or degrading when it is worthy, but such toil as that known to European peasants was little better than slavery. The labor which free American farmers of the early nineteenth century performed in their fields was no less physically taxing. The soil was prepared with a primitive plow, seeding and cultivating were done by hand, reaping was accomplished by the sickle and the scythe, or at most by the cradle. Crops were produced by sunshine and by rain and by the straining muscles of weary men.

To appreciate the force of the stirring circumstances that kept pace with Cyrus Hall McCormick throughout his life, it is necessary to know that he was of Scotch-Irish ancestry. His blood was the same as that which dared to fight and suffer for the Scotch covenant of faith and which, transplanted to Ireland, made Ulster prosperous. When the British armies pursued the exiles to Ireland, a full half-million of them emigrated to America. Broken in fortune but whole in spirit, they brought with them an inheritance of liberty, of industry, and of conscience sympathetic toward the growing ideals of the New World.

One of these Scotch-Irishmen was Thomas McCormick, who came to America in 1734. His son Robert moved from Pennsylvania to Virginia and later fought in the War for Independence. Robert's son, who was to become the father of Cyrus, was also named Robert. In 1808, he married Mary Ann Hall, a true daughter of the faith-spurred, embattled Scotch-Irish strain. Thus Cyrus' ancestry had done its best to prosper him by providing him a subconscious store of courage and faith and perseverance and vision such as few people have proved themselves worthy to hold.

Before they were expelled from Ulster, these people exhibited a skill at labor that has left the north of Ireland prosperous even to this day. They were among the most industrious, moral, and intelligent groups of people in Britain. They were fine farmers, skilled weavers, constructive builders; and when they came to America, they carried their arts and their tools and their energies with them. The first Robert McCormick was a weaver as well as a farmer. Patrick Hall, Mary Ann's father, was a leader of that strict Presbyterianism which thought that even hymn music was out of place in the kirk. Robert, the father of Cyrus, was an educated, prosperous land-owner, who, besides his farms, operated gristmills, saw-mills, a smelter, a distillery, and a blacksmith shop. He was a reader and a student, gentle but energetic, an active churchman, and was wide in his interests. His mechanical ingenuity made him an indefatigable inventor. Also, perhaps, he was something of a dreamer. Cyrus' mother was imaginative, more constructively ambitious than her husband; shrewd, and imbued with the typical Scotch-Irish desire to improve herself and the world around her. Cyrus inherited all these qualities from his ancestors and to them he added an indomitable will that transcended the stubbornness of his race. The Scotch-Irish inheritance and the characters of his mother and father were all blended in his being. But men to be great must add something to the mental equipment with which they are born. These qualities in his case were: will to drive through the present and imagination to see through to the future.

Cyrus Hall McCormick was born February 15, 1809, on the family farm, Walnut Grove, in Rockbridge County, Virginia. There was no public fanfare over the event, but the star of destiny must have been shining brightly. That was a great year for the world. Poe and Tennyson, Chopin and Mendelssohn, Darwin, Gladstone, and great Lincoln were born then — and McCormick, if he may be judged by his services to humanity, is none too small a man to share their birth-year.

As a boy, Cyrus went to the Old Field School. It is not

recorded how he progressed in the Three R's, the Shorter Catechism, and the Bible, but there is a tale to the effect that he astounded his teacher by constructing an accurate hemispherical map of the world. When he was fifteen, he found that his boyish physique was insufficient to swing a heavy cradle in the harvest grain; so he made a smaller implement to suit his slight muscles.

At eighteen, he made himself some needed surveying instruments. Of greater importance was his invention of a hillside plow, his first major contribution to modern agriculture. It is also certain that he was in constant attendance on his father's labor in the blacksmith shop. Perhaps throughout his youth he felt stirring in himself the inquiring, earnest urge to create, which the natural unrestraint of life in America made possible. The great inventions of those times were the product of social and mental vigor as well as of economic necessity.

Between 1809 and 1816, Robert McCormick made the first of several attempts to build a mechanical reaper. Like the devices of others who had interested themselves in the problem, his machine was pushed ahead into the grain by two horses and the wheat was to be thrust against stationary convex sickles by rapidly revolving beaters. Unfortunately, it utterly failed to cut the grain, so Robert abandoned it. At various times during the next fifteen years, he made other fruitless attempts to revive his scheme. His eldest son was informed as to his ideas and may have helped him prepare his last machine for its unsuccessful trial in May, 1831. It actually cut some green wheat fairly well. But previous inventors had already succeeded in doing this, though no one had been able to handle the wheat after the cutting. Robert's machine flung it away from his knives in a matted tangle of straw. The problem was too difficult for him.

There are many family legends how Cyrus helped his father with this last machine, and how, in the same year, 1831, Robert encouraged his son toward the reaper that was so soon to turn a page of history. The probability, however, is that the younger man had little contact with Robert's efforts except to profit by his father's failures. Without question he learned from them what pitfalls to avoid. Robert's work inspired his son's interest in the problem of mechanical harvesting, and the father's fine craftsmanship taught Cyrus to work with tools. In the farm blacksmith shop he found an outlet for the ideas germinating within him.

Cyrus must have started on his own machine as soon as he saw the evidence of his father's admitted failure. Between May and July, he conceived his own new principles, built one or more models, and developed a machine which cut grain successfully. He found within his heart the vigor necessary to do this colossal task inside of six short weeks.

Without doubt his experiments were aided by the fact that from his boyhood he had been engaged in practical farming. He knew that it would serve no useful purpose to provide a machine that would cut grain only under ideal conditions. Wheat beaten down by rain or tangled by wind was an ever-present problem. The straw might be damp or dry. Harvest is a necessity dictated by Nature, not a holiday planned by man. Perhaps, even, he was served by the fact that he was so entirely ignorant of previous reaper investigations in other parts of the world. His mind was fresh. He did not know that for years many men had been toiling to solve the problem of the reaper, or that before his time many futile reaper patents had been issued in England and America. He had never heard of Pitt's work nearly fifty years before, nor of Bell and Ogle, nor did he know of Manning who had already patented certain of the features he was to discover for himself and incorporate in his own machine. His sole experience was with his father's unsuccessful attempt; his prime asset was the power of his own tremendous will driving his imagination on to accomplishment.

It is not strange that no news of these other men had sifted through to him. In these days of instant and constant communication, it is difficult to imagine the isolation of that truly backwoods community in the Virginia mountains. There were no railroads, no canals, nothing but clay roads leading to the peopled centers of the State. The Scotch-Irish people of the neighborhood were self-sufficient in every way; they neither knew nor cared about the outside world. And yet Cyrus' brain had overleaped the blue ridges, had grappled with problems as to which he had only local experience, had flown out to speculate on a world-wide need. He had the soul of greatness within him, he possessed that genius which lifts the giants of history above the world of average men.

He set to work in the old log blacksmith shop, cutting and fashioning wood and bending into shape the few iron pieces of the machine. His first reaper was built in six weeks at most. He tried it out privately in an adjacent wheatfield on the farm, with none but the members of his family for spectators. Becoming convinced that he was on the right road, he set to work feverishly to remodel it for a public test. The initial machine of early July had a straight-edged reciprocating knife actuated by gears from a main wheel, a platform extending sideways from the wheel, shafts for a single horse, an outside divider to separate the standing grain from that to be gathered into the cutter bar, and fingers to project in front of the blade. The late July machine had an improved divider, a better

THE BLACKSMITH SHOP OF WALNUT GROVE FARM IN
WHICH McCORMICK BUILT HIS REAPER IN 1831
The shop still stands

cutter bar provided with saw-tooth, incised serrations along its leading edge, and a reel to hold the grain in front of the knife.

During his work Cyrus was encouraged by his mother who adored him and by his father who, though he may have despaired because of his own failure, could not but have thrilled as he saw his son's machine grow piece by piece. The boy's courage and tenacity gave him hope. Two particular friends watched the reaper develop. One of these was Colonel James McDowell, who shared Cyrus' optimism. The other, Captain William Massie, was a skeptic until the success of the first trial, after which he became so enthusiastic that when times grew hard for the inventor he opened his purse to him. Most of all, the name of his Negro helper, Jo Anderson, deserves honor as the man who worked beside him in the building of the reaper. Jo Anderson was a slave, a general farm laborer and a friend. Cyrus never spared his own fine physique by day or by night; and the Negro toiled with him up to the hour of the test and after. It is pleasant to know that in later times, when old Jo's productive days were over, Cyrus or his son provided for his declining years.

McCormick's contribution to the well-being of the world was real. Men needed him. However much we may pride ourselves on our modernity, we are still too prone to put our sole faith in the test of use. Even now, in spite of our worship of new deeds, we still let genius frighten us. We love to place our reliance on the tried and true methods other men before us have proved to be secure. We are served by the fact that some few men, like Cyrus Hall McCormick, are brave enough to look ahead and wonder.

We of to-day pay too little attention to the work of those early men who labored that we may live. We wear too boldly the garments of experience, and fail to realize how much we owe to the past, however unprogressive it may seem. Five thousand years ago in Egypt, agriculture was the leading industry of a civilization which was just dawning. The early Egyptian knew how to grow cotton for his clothes, and grain and legumes for his food. He had found out, furthermore, how to breed plants to better their variety, and he understood the seasons. It is even possible that he had a dim perception of crop rotation. Doubtless he thought himself up-to-date.

But such farm tools as he had were rudimentary in the extreme. Mostly, they were made of wood, for metal was still rare enough to be preserved for weapons or for carving stone. The first garden tool of prehistoric man was probably nothing more than a crooked stick with which he picked and hacked at the soil until it was broken and pulverized enough for planting. But in Egypt, some one had already invented the rudimentary spade or hoe, the familiar wood plow, and the reaping hook. When the harvest was ready, the Egyptian reaped his grain with the curved blade which some brilliant mind had discovered would cut so much more easily than a straight knife. The very first invention of an agricultural implement may well have been the primitive plow, which could be pulled through the ground by slaves or draft animals. However rudimentary it may have been, it lightened somewhat the farmer's labor. Even at that early date, our ancestors were interesting themselves in finding out how to accomplish desired results with less effort.

Agriculture was vital to Egyptian prosperity. There was little game in the surrounding desert. Cattle and the increasing numbers of a growing population had to be fed. The first recorded trading expeditions to the outside world brought back tiger skins and ostrich plumes to adorn the reigning sovereign, but they also brought back new plants for the farms of Egypt. However crude the tools of agricultural production may have been, it is interesting to note that they were important enough in the minds of Egyptians to cause the adoption of both the plow and the reaping hook as symbols in the first alphabet.

I well remember when one day, some twenty years ago, I was standing by an Egyptian obelisk trying to puzzle out the meaning of the ancient hieroglyphics carved on its granite sides. I was particularly interested in the conventionalized symbol of a plow. All at once there arose a great clatter of straining animals and shouting men. I saw a team of white oxen drawing a plow, tilling the field around the obelisk. I looked from the fifteenth-century B.C. hieroglyphic to the twentieth-century A.D. plow and back again. They were identical: thirty-three hundred years had passed, but agricultural machinery had stood still. Egypt was preparing its soil as it had done in the days of the Pharaohs. A whole world of progress had been born in the meantime. Plato, Archimedes, Cæsar, Galileo, Newton, Darwin, had lived and died. The Western nations had passed into the most modern epoch. But agriculture, in Egypt at least, had remained unchanged and unchanging while the world moved on.

It is not necessary to look to Egypt to find examples of the slight growth of agriculture before 1831. The peasants of Europe, even as late as the eighteenth century, were serfs of the soil. The fact that a mediæval manuscript may show an illustration of an isolated attempt to construct a wagon-box grain drill does not mean that men employed usable machinery. However much social life was enriched by sculptured churches or the neo-classic literature of the Renaissance or the songs of the troubadours, or the rising political strength of England, agriculturists still lived a life of dreary toil. Wooden plows they had, but seeding, cultivating, harvesting, and threshing all depended on the muscular energy of two-legged beasts of burden called men.

The primitive methods of olden times survive even to this day in isolated or backward communities. The Pueblo Indians of New Mexico and Arizona have modern plows and other agricultural implements, it is true, but they put reliance in the prayer-dances of their forefathers. Rice in Java and in much of China is raised by methods that have not changed since history began. The walls of irrigation terraces are built with a clumsy hoe, the rice is planted by hand, and it is reaped with a little knife as long as your finger. The Indians of our own Southwest and the natives of the Orient produce their crops mainly by trust in Nature and the muscular effort of bent backs.

In all the centuries before 1831, there had been invented but two new agricultural implements for harvesting, the scythe in the sixteenth century and the cradle in the eighteenth. This was a large scythe with wooden fingers fastened to the back of the blade in such a way that the cut grain fell on them and was deposited in a swath on the ground. The cradle was heavier than the scythe, and, except as certain skilled harvesters learned to swing it with a rhythm corresponding to the momentum of its weight, harder to use successfully. But the grain fell from it in regular rows instead of the tangled, scattered bunches left by the scythes; so when the binders came along they could make better speed.

At the best, though, harvest was a period of drudgery. A long line of crouching men stooping across a field, a scorching sun beating on their backs, arms swinging heavy knives into tough grain, muscles tensing to lift and drop burdens, slaves of fear struggling to avert famine — this

was what harvest labor meant to farmers before the age
of machinery. Such heartbreaking effort was nothing
more than sodden drudgery. Obviously, it may have been
spiritually possible for a farmer to fix his attention so
keenly upon bread, the object for which he was striving,
that he could keep ahead of weariness; but how many of
us are mentally detached enough to forget our own mis-
eries? Labor is honorable; labor in combination with
thought is an inspiration. But toil without hope is degrading, and work so exhausting that it cripples a man's
body saps his brain as well.

Cyrus Hall McCormick was a Virginia farmer. Such
speculation upon the historical background of relief from
toil lay beyond his Scotch-Irish ken. However much he
may have realized in later life the importance of his invention, in 1831 he knew nothing more than that harvest
labor was too hard. His was the part of striving that
other men might rest.

The historic little shop where he built the first successful reaper is standing to-day. It is a small square log
building on a high stone foundation. Inside is the forge,
a littered workbench, the hewn section of a tree, and
the old stone anvil. There is one small window, and two
doors. The walls and ceiling are black with the smoke of
a thousand fires. Old walnut trees stand beside the shop
and cast their shadows impartially over the past and into
the future. Not far away is the homestead, a chaste brick
building with the pleasing, provincial lines of a sincere
architecture. Tall trees hang over the house and flower
beds surround it — for Mary Ann Hall McCormick, her
son said in later years, was a skilled gardener. Beyond
the lawns a wide field dips down into a hollow and then
climbs up to a wooded height. In the distance are the
misty summits of the Blue Ridge Mountains. In sum-

mer, when the sun is pouring into the Valley and over the nodding heads of yellow wheat, the scene is very peaceful, very beautiful — just as, doubtless, it was on that July day of 1831.

That was a day when famine was ordered from the land and the drudgery of old agriculture was banished. But when I stand there after the passing of a century, my mind is content to dwell on the inventor, on the man. I am aware of the great facts that now farmers all over the world are directing machinery instead of spending muscle, and that there is bread for the multitude and a sure relief from famine. But as I contemplate these benefits, I see a boy reach out his hand to unlock the future. Hope buoys him, though he is weary. Hour after hour, day after day, far into the night he has been working, carving wood and hammering iron, planning and scheming, creating. Perhaps for a moment he looks up from his bench. Beyond the smithy window is a field of ripe grain. He smiles: he is ready. His reaper clatters on into history. He strides after it along the broad highway of service to humanity.

CHAPTER II

THE DEVELOPMENT OF THE INVENTION

THE significance of the 1831 test of the original reaper is not that Cyrus Hall McCormick's machine cut grain. Judging from the harvest standards of to-day, it is certain that it did not perform perfectly. But then, for the first time in all history, a mechanical reaper cut grain and at the same time included in its being the fundamental elements essential to proper harvesting. Whatever the present world has since added to the science of agricultural equipment, no modern grain-cutting machine can suffice without the elements around which Cyrus Hall McCormick's reaper was organized. These essential principles were seven:

The straight reciprocating knife, whereby the standing grain would be attacked by lateral motion as well as by the forward movement of the machine. (This the inventor himself regarded as the most vital of the elements.)

The fingers or guards for the knife, which supported the grain at the moment of cutting.

The reel, which gathered the grain in front of the reaper and held the heads in place as the fingers held the stalks.

The platform, on which the severed grain might fall to be raked away in a swath.

The main wheel, directly behind the horse, which carried the machine and operated gears to actuate the moving parts.

The principle of cutting to one side of the line of

draft, which permitted the horse to walk on the stubble while the cutter bar worked in the standing grain.

The divider at the outer end of the cutter bar, to divide the standing grain from that which was to be reaped.

In 1831 and for several years thereafter, Cyrus had not the slightest idea that he was not the sole and original discoverer of every one of these cardinal elements. Actually he initiated them all independently and alone. But it is possible to find suggestions made by previous inventors which closely resemble individual parts of the McCormick machine. These prior suggestions were in no case parts of an operative reaper. They were theoretical constructions, many of which were never tried in the field. In the case of six of Cyrus' elements he was unconsciously duplicating the prior discoveries of other inventors. The principle of the single main wheel alone was absolutely original with him. Nevertheless, even if there had been no originality in any of the seven features, his reaper was still a true invention. It is a well settled rule of patent law that an invention need actually be no more than a new combination of kr.cwn features to produce a novel and useful result and be a true discovery.

The seven elements which were now for the first time included in one device were the result of that practical genius which we call invention. They seem simple because they are so really great. Obviously, as time wore on, each one of them could be improved upon, and other principles were to be added to the list. Nevertheless, each one of the seven is to be found in machines that now harvest grain, even in the combined harvester-thresher of 1931. A century of progress has passed, but the

WORKING REPLICA OF THE ORIGINAL REAPER

original features live on, the old truths remain. Grain binders are now pulled by a tractor, where the first reaper was dragged along by a single horse. Their mechanistic speed is more than that of the first crude implement, their endurance is greater because of the smooth polish of bearings whose steel had not even been invented a short hundred years ago, their service is better because of the wider knowledge of the protagonists of modern machinery.

Cyrus Hall McCormick would have been the first to admit that his reaper of 1831 was no more than a beginning. To think that any invention, at any time or place, springs full-grown and complete from the mind of man is an egregious error. An inventor's second guess is usually better than his first; and, if he has the genius to conceive the first step, he must, if he is really great, have also the critical judgment to see wherein his work falls short of perfection. Thus, Cyrus was not even satisfied enough with his effort to patent it until 1834, nor did he begin to seek a market for it until 1840.

After a journey to Kentucky in his father's interests, he returned to Walnut Grove in the spring of 1832 and set to work to improve his original reaper. With new fingers, an adjustable platform, and improved gearing, the machine again faced the ordeal of public trial at Lexington. But the owner of the field was not pleased when too much grain was knocked off and fell on the ground. He ordered Cyrus and his reaper off. One William Taylor, the owner of an adjoining stand of grain, pulled down the intervening rail fence and invited the young man to continue the demonstration. Some cradle-wielding laborers jeered, but during the afternoon the reaper harvested six acres of wheat. A school principal pompously announced that the reaper was worth a hundred thousand dollars, whereupon Cyrus dryly remarked that he would gladly sell it for half as much. But the machine was accorded the honor of exhibition in the courthouse square.

The experiments continued during 1833. Cyrus built another, larger reaper, and with it and the 1832 model he cut the Walnut Grove grain as well as the wheat of several neighbors. His patron, McDowell, even bought a machine, but this may have been nothing more than a friendly gesture, for it was later returned. A newspaper article describing its success around Lexington carried the reaper's fame abroad. This article and certain farmers' testimonials which were included were reprinted in other periodicals, even in far-away New York. For the first time McCormick's renown and the story of his accomplishment went out into the world. Even a quiet Virginia valley is not too distant a birthplace for the kind of greatness that is universal.

The reaper was patented in 1834. It seems that Cyrus did not yet wish to take so conclusive a step, and he obviously had no desire to seek a commercial market for a device which he still regarded as imperfect. But in April he saw in a magazine a picture of a reaper patented the previous autumn by Obed Hussey. Here was a rival, and without doubt McCormick desired to establish the fact of his own priority and protect his interests. So he applied for and was granted a patent.

But even so, Cyrus knew that his work was by no means done. Farmers would write glowing testimonials about the reaper, but they would not buy. Friends sought him out to advise him to apply his active brain to something else. Who would have blamed him if he had become discouraged? He did not weaken, yet for a time he laid the reaper aside and gave his energy to assisting in the development of certain of his father's inventions, such as a threshing machine and a hemp-brake. Also, he may have resumed the promotion of his own early hillside plows. He had advertised and sold some of these as early as 1831, and it probably seemed more re-munerative at the moment to engage in this reasonably sure commerce than to go on pushing the adoption of the reaper. As a matter of fact, the hills and valleys of his neighborhood made too many fields ill-suited to a reaper.

In addition to work in the shop, he began to operate on his own account a farm his father had given him. He used his machines in his harvesting, but he had no time to develop them nor was he encouraged to do so. Even Robert grew skeptical of the commercial value of the reaper, and advised him to stick to the surer emoluments of farming. But Cyrus could not forget mechanics and invention. He secured the aid of his father and a neighbor to build a furnace and engage in making pig iron. For a while he prospered, but by 1839 the effects of the panic of 1837 bore down on his little industry. Father and son were wiped out in the collapse of the price of iron. Half of their land went to their creditors, the rest was mort-gaged, and nothing remained but the reaper patent which nobody wanted.

During these difficult years there developed a beautiful intimacy and a complete understanding between father and son. Robert's fine mind and his possibly impractical, speculative curiosity was transmuted in Cyrus into prac-tical determination and constructive logic. Robert's reaper had been unsuccessful, whereas Cyrus' cut grain. The young man was an energetic driver; the older was a dreamer who, with any other than Scotch-Irish ancestry, might have been a mystic. And yet, however different they may have been, they were glad to work side by side in a common cause. Because the father could not be sanguine of the commercial value of his son's reaper, Cyrus worked to perfect Robert's ideas; because Cyrus could not confine the active power of his mind within a limited field, Robert helped him into business. In later years when the reaper was beginning to be more of a success, the inventor regarded his father as something more than a partner. They achieved a firm friendship out of their relationship. When Robert died, Cyrus for the first time in his busy life felt the numbing shock of utter aloneness.

After the pig-iron disaster, Cyrus resurrected his old machines and, this time under the pressure of imminent bankruptcy, resumed the work that was to fill his life. He had discovered on his own farm that the reaper's most serious defect was in the cutting apparatus. Now he turned his particular attention to the edge of the knife. Where the original reaper had been equipped with a knife, on the front edge of which serrations had been cut all running on the same diagonal, the machines built after 1840 were provided with groups of serrations opposed one to the other — that is to say, they ran to the right for an inch and a half, then to the left for a similar distance, then to the right, and so on. The present type of cutter bar, with separate, riveted-on cutting sections, was not developed until 1851.

In 1840, also, Cyrus made his first real reaper sales. The tottering family finances made it necessary for him to get an income from his invention. He sold one reaper to a farmer who rode in from the northern part of the State and one to a man from the James River district. Yet it is on record that he also refused to sell a third which would have been doomed to failure because it would have to operate in drenched grain. The two

CYRUS HALL McCORMICK IN HIS THIRTIES
From a daguerreotype

machines sold did not work well; so he spent the harvest period of 1841 in private experiments. By the next year he had so improved the cutting efficiency of the knife by changing the angle of the serrations that he was able to sell seven reapers in 1842. The volume of sales rose to twenty-nine in 1843 and to fifty in 1844. The price of the reaper was one hundred dollars.

Newspaper articles began to be printed about the reaper and usually they were favorable to the new mechanism. The statement was published abroad that it would save half the cost of harvesting. One of McCormick's machines with eight men to bind could reap as much as five scythemen and ten helpers. Also, there was less loss through shattered grain than with the swinging cradle. If the machine were well made, the principle proved its soundness.

All the early machines were built in the blacksmith shop on the Walnut Grove farm. Cyrus had no other factory. He not only had to supervise such workmen as he employed, but he must himself do any work that required particular care. To sell his product, he had to ride for miles and days over mountain roads. He had to learn to watch credits and supervise collections. He alone could secure materials, arrange for drayage to the nearest canal, do all those things that now require the services of department heads and organization. That was in truth the age of individualism!

It was also in 1843 that his famous controversy with Obed Hussey began. Hussey, it will be remembered, had been granted a patent on a reaper in 1833. He was a whimsical sailor whose hobby it was to work at mechanical problems. It is said that a friend asked him why he did not make a reaper. 'What,' said Hussey, 'isn't there such a thing?' — and forthwith set out to invent one.

When he succeeded and had patented his device, he sold reapers in the district around his home in Cincinnati. On hearing of the Hussey patent, Cyrus published a warning not to infringe on an already occupied field. Hussey, nevertheless, invaded the East, established himself at Baltimore, and challenged McCormick to a field test. The temper of the competition may be judged from a letter which Cyrus wrote a few years later to his brother, when he said, 'Meet Hussey in Maryland *and put him down.*'

However many reaper makers there were a few years later, Hussey and McCormick were then alone in the field. Each claimed the advantage of priority and superior performance. Each bombarded the press with praises of his own machine and scathing comments on the futility of the rival device. Yet finally when they met the result was inconclusive. Hussey's reaper was smaller and would not operate in wet grain. McCormick's was manifestly stronger, but broke down when he became too sanguine of its ability to perform unnecessary tasks. They both finished the test, and the judges decided narrowly in favor of McCormick. Spectators stated, however, that Hussey's machine was simpler, which may very well have been true, since it was not equipped with the essential features of the reel and divider. It was really the progenitor of the modern mower.

Subsequent investigation proved Hussey's patent to be sound and not in conflict with McCormick's. Many years later, when he had retired from competition, he won damages for an infringement against the shape of his finger guards. Hussey's reaper was more of a factor in newspaper debate than in the field, but for a long time he pursued Cyrus and annoyed him with charge and countercharge. But however bitter a critic Hussey was, he was an honest old warrior. He invariably refused to equip his reaper with a reel because he had not himself invented one. He opposed Cyrus' patents frantically, but when he heard the incontrovertible evidence of the public exhibitions of 1831 and 1832, he startled the examiners by flatly admitting his rival's priority.

In those early days of American business, competition meant warfare to the bitter end. There was no quarter given or expected. Men fought for their rights or lost them. Hussey was a picturesque debater, but he was no business man. He sold a certain number of his machines, particularly along the Atlantic seaboard, and he even competed abroad in later years. But he could never stand against the business genius which Cyrus was soon to add to his inventive faculty.

The early inventors are hardly to be blamed for so bitterly contesting each advantage they could claim. They were so much alone, they had so much to do, and the commercial prize ahead of them seemed so limited. McCormick had one great quality Hussey did not share: he had vision to see far beyond the horizon of Virginia. In 1844, he sold reapers in New York, Tennessee, Ohio, Indiana, Illinois, Wisconsin, and Missouri, as well as in his home country. The West was calling and he answered.

As soon as the Virginia harvest of that year was over, the inventor decided to investigate for himself the Western States from which the unexpected business was trickling in. He traveled to New York, and then on through Wisconsin, Illinois, into Missouri, and back to Ohio. He was astounded at the expanse of wide fields he saw, so different from the narrower valleys of his home. His imagination was challenged. He wrote to his family that reapers were luxuries in Virginia, but were necessities in Ohio, Illinois, and on the great plains of the West. He understood immediately that inland Virginia would never do as a center from which to distribute his machines to farms along the Mississippi River. From Indiana he wrote, 'It seems wrong to pay $20 or $25 freight... when they might be made in the West — considering, too, the greater uncertainty of shipping.'

He began immediately to contemplate the thought of moving his entire business to some place in the West. He did not have to look back many years to the time when men of his own kind, Scotch-Irish pioneers, had moved across the frontier and out into the wilderness. What they had done in their field of endeavor, he could do in his. They had battled with the unknown to return and bring back with them tales of virgin soil and unlimited horizons. He and his reaper could follow in aid of the brave settler-crusaders who had pressed on into the plains just behind the explore.

In preparation for the ultimate move to Chicago, he went to Brockport, New York, on the Erie Canal, and sold a license to manufacture reapers to Seymour and Morgan. He sent his brother Leander, now a young man of twenty-eight and able to fit himself into the growing business, to Cincinnati after making a similar contract. This enlarged production allowed a greater volume of sales; so he himself and such county agents as he had appointed sold 123 machines in 1845. The next year his sales mounted still further. In 1847, he moved to Chicago.

In the meantime his interest in improving his machine had never waned. It had passed the experimental stage in that the reaper would unquestionably cut grain successfully. He secured two other patents, one in 1845 and one in 1847, and the wooden implement of the thirties became McCormick's Patent Virginia Reaper, a two-horse machine with a wider cut and a seat at the side whereon the raker sat as he worked. In 1848, he applied for an extension of his original patent.

It will be remembered that the original McCormick patent was granted in 1834. This patent ran for fourteen years, but as no attempt had been made to exploit it even in a small way until 1840, the inventor had enjoyed no more than eight years of protection. During that time, he testified in the patent hearing which followed, he had sold 778 machines at a profit of $20 each and had disposed of territorial sales rights for a total gross profit of $22,643. But the Brockport licensees, Seymour and Morgan, felt that their profits would be larger if the extension were refused and the patent was free; and they had strong political influence. They fostered a cleverly organized counter-campaign of farmer publicity.

The story of the patent battle which followed would fill a volume. Hussey and McCormick were again aligned against each other; patent attorneys wrote to farmers to rise against the royalty charge of the reaper monopoly; the farm press was filled with columns of arguments; petitions were circulated indiscriminately. The patent board rejected McCormick's application, and it was said that his invention was of too much value to the public to remain in private hands. He caused the matter to be taken to Congress, where the case became a *cause célèbre*. An anti-McCormick lobby was organized, public opinion in New York was fostered by the Brockport manufacturers, and the farmers of the country were said to be up in arms. Ultimately, the patent extension was denied; so McCormick lost, just as he was to lose almost all of the many lawsuits in which he engaged. He emerged without protection from the patent laws, but the debate had established clearly the fact of his priority as the original inventor and it had put the stamp of governmental approbation on the economic value of his reaper.

History has since proved that the patent-extension battle was futile. McCormick pushed on to success without the protection he thought was essential; the Brockport manufacturers had gained the right to make reapers, but they were not able enough to exercise it widely. He knew how to organize an invention into a business and they did not. He possessed the creative genius to find ways of making the reaper available for all farmers.

To remove to Chicago in those days necessitated the stern courage of the frontier fighter. The raw little city in the swamps by Lake Michigan had in 1847 a population of only seventeen thousand. Land values had collapsed after an early boom, and a welter of mud and disease made the town appear ridiculous to its neighbors. There were few paved streets, the houses were frame shacks, there were nothing but broken plankroads through the swamps to the surrounding land, and the harbor was obstructed by sandbars. But Chicago was the center of a great area of rich land, a canal to the west was about to be opened, and immigrants were flocking in. It had little to offer in the way of material comfort, but it was a city of opportunity.

Among the several firms which McCormick had licensed to build reapers was Gray and Warner, of Chicago, manufacturers of cradles. For a time Gray became his partner and together they built five hundred machines for the harvest of 1848. Then Gray quarreled with McCormick over the terms of the partnership and sold out to William B. Ogden, that great pioneer of early

Chicago, and W. E. Jones. The firm name was McCormick, Ogden & Company. Ogden was rich for those days, and his confidence in the future of Chicago and the West was unbounded. But he also possessed a strong temperament, too strong to harmonize with the fiery zeal of McCormick's nature. Also, the one was absorbed in his reaper, while the other had wide interests in every activity that touched Chicago. By 1849, they agreed amicably to disagree, and McCormick bought the Ogden and Jones half of the business for $65,000. Fifteen hundred machines had been sold that year and he had made enough money to pay so large a price: already, at forty years of age, the Virginia farmer boy had become a captain of young industry.

Some have said that Cyrus Hall McCormick was a lucky speculator who rode to success on the wave of energy that developed the West. This was the point of view of jealous English competitors. Americans have accorded him the honor of making the development of the West possible.

So long as the reaping hook and the cradle were the instruments of agricultural production, the yield of the fields was limited to the amount of labor available. Before the reaper, a scytheman could with infinite toil harvest barely two or three acres of grain each day. In 1845, Ohio and Pennsylvania were the leading wheat States. The West was still remote and isolated. Illinois was raising five million bushels of wheat each year, but its own consumption, plus its exportable surplus, was far less than that. Because of lack of labor, much of the crop could not be harvested and was given over to cattle and hogs turned in to feed on golden wheat.

After 1849, the rumor of the discovery of gold in California made matters worse. Thousands left the East to make the long journey overland in search of easy riches. Commodity prices rose in reaction to the new supply of bullion and such laborers as remained drew double wages. The farmers of the Middle West, cut off as yet from easy rail transportation, were helpless. The reaper appeared at the eleventh hour and allowed them not only to produce wheat for a rapidly expanding population, but, by substituting machinery for expensive or non-existent labor, to reduce the cost of their production and live through.

McCormick was quick to see what the discovery of California gold meant for him. Where he might easily himself have followed the prairie road into the setting sun, he preferred to pin his faith to another golden future, the future of wheat. He preferred to see himself a partner of those men who would not be lured away and of those sons of theirs who, in future generations when there was no more gold in California, would be harvesting the world's bread all through the prairies of the West. He spread advertisements abroad predicting a shortage of farm labor and telling how his reaper would relieve that problem. While his brothers attended to the little brick factory by the Chicago River, he rode endlessly over the plains, spying out the homes of future farmers and preaching the gospel of the reaper. He knew no rest, no ease. He was experiencing the cost of service to an ideal.

But, after all, when have Scotch-Irishmen ever counted the cost? They were driven to Ulster for their faith. They were driven thence to America, and took with them the hard-working zeal which was the foundation-stone of their prosperity. In America they sought the frontier and all its trials. They conquered the wilderness by their ability. Doubtless they did not appreciate the full destiny of their pioneering, but whatever of it they saw, they did. Cyrus Hall McCormick drew from his blood his courage, his stubborn tenacity, and his native ability. He added thereto an unbounded force of will that leaped at obstacles whenever they appeared, and the clear vision of imagination that saw beyond each barrier a prize.

He was a product of sterling inheritance and the dynamic compulsion of new times. The eighteenth century had vanished, individualism was beginning to be bruited abroad, submerged peoples and personalities were stirring. The millions who had been toiling were somehow feeling the influence of new democracy. Democracy was born in the American War for Independence and grew up in Europe in the first half of the nineteenth century. It flourished robustly in the United States because the country was free and new. Even to-day Americans are young enough to tolerate experiments.

People have lived through stirring times during the last hundred years. Wars have continued because we have not quite been able to free ourselves from outworn methods and bygone rules of conduct. But we have advanced. We have used such advantage as we might gain from five thousand years of history; and we are conscious of a wider horizon and an unfettered thought. Many men are now able to try to develop new ideas where formerly only a few had the vision to do so. Many men have claimed the right to become individuals instead of a pathetic few. We of the younger generation speak of modernism and try to explain it and defend it. What we really mean is that the nineteenth century taught the twentieth to think for itself.

The whole sphere of political science has been restudied in the light of experimental democracy. In the nineteenth century the entire field of economics was plowed almost for the first time. Intellectual and social worth developed amazingly in reaction to the dimly seen hope of relief from toil. Soon men would no longer have to break their hearts in the fields and in tiny shops: the dawn would break as soon as machinery could be devised to lighten labor. New thoughts were beginning to stir in the minds of those few teachers who could show the many how to use their minds instead of their muscles. The stage of free events was set for Cyrus Hall McCormick and the great men of his time. They were to make the twentieth century possible by their vigorous leadership, their organizing ability, their grand succession of new practices and new thought, and their radiating glamour of success. They shattered every old manner of life. They made a new world wide and fine enough for the unleashed power of modern times.

CHAPTER III

THE INVENTION OF A BUSINESS

CYRUS HALL McCORMICK invented the reaper and thus, out of an undying service to humanity, achieved fame enough for any man. The reaper is his chief claim to recognition in the eyes of posterity. But until recent years it was not sufficiently recognized that, even at its inception, the invention bore within its loins the seeds, not only of modern agriculture, but of modern industry as well.

Freedom from almost universal slavery to the soil had to be achieved before man could liberate himself from the narrow limitations which hand labor set upon his other occupations. McCormick made relief possible. He must also be acclaimed as one of the inventors of modern business and of the benefits it has brought to the factory worker and to the consuming public. He was a pioneer of mass production and of waste-saving methods of manufacture. He conceived of utterly unheard-of means of mass distribution such as advertising, public demonstration, and warranty of product. His competitors thought him visionary. When he put into practice certain schemes, since fundamental to the sale of agricultural implements, such as credit to his customers, his friends predicted his certain downfall. But he forged ahead, and his business, founded on the same determined vision that produced the reaper, was to live after him.

How grandly McCormick wrought during the latter half of his life to accomplish this will become apparent when one remembers that, just as he began to be effective as a manufacturer, he was deprived of patent protection.

Instead of facing the world with a secure monopoly at his back, he saw a horde of competitors rising up on every side to meet him with copies of his own device. A McCormick reaper, he had a right to fear, would perform just as satisfactorily under any other name. Seymour and Morgan, his former licensees, had led the battle against the extension of his 1834 patent. They had manufactured many of the reapers that had been built; and now that the field was open to the public, they were hard at work producing duplicates of McCormick's machine. Hussey, also deprived of his own patent protection, was still in the field and had not yet yielded to McCormick. William F. Ketchum, who was later to lead the early mower world, was obtaining patents and building machines. The Fountain brothers and H. F. Mann were placing on the market McCormick reapers to which their own devices had been added. Altogether there were by the end of 1850 at least thirty reaper firms which had taken the basic principles of McCormick's invention as a starting-point and were seeking to add something new. Each year new manufacturers were springing up who were building copies or adaptations of the Virginia reaper. The prospect was not pleasant for a man who knew that his was the original invention and bitterly resented the fact that an unkind government had denied him further protection just when his patent rights were beginning to be valuable.

In connection with his application for a patent extension, McCormick testified in 1848 that all told he had built no more than 778 reapers, including 500 made with Gray in Chicago in 1848. Fifteen hundred were built in 1849 during the Ogden partnership. Small as such quantities may seem, they gave him a long lead over his competitors which he was never to relinquish. He bequeathed to his successors a start that kept them in the supreme position he had won — and yet he did this without patent protection.

There remains an illuminating letter written to him in 1859 by his beloved brother William on the event of the refusal of the patent commissioners to extend his second patent. William understood his elder brother better than any other man and, out of his rare prescience, was able to value correctly the real basis of his success. He wrote, 'Your money has been made not out of your patents but by making and selling the machines.' Cyrus' business continued to grow in the face of free and widespread competition, not because of his genius as an inventor, which could now be drawn upon by all and sundry desiring to copy him, but because of his skill, his boldness, and his business acumen. Alone among the inventors of his period, he was able to create a business.

Cyrus Hall McCormick was to become the leading industrialist of his generation. In a day before the birth of anything resembling a factory system, his prophetic vision recognized the need for a factory of his own. It is related that he raged at the damage both to his own reputation and to farmers' crops caused by the inefficient operation of a poorly built reaper thrown together regardless of quality by one of his licensed manufacturers. Ever conscious of the harvest needs of his farmer customers, he knew his reaper could not succeed unless the same ideals of service which he had adopted as his creed were built into it. Therefore, after he was free from the limitations imposed on his aggressive temperament by the partnerships of 1848 and 1849, he preferred to forge ahead by himself. As soon as existing licensing agreements expired, he saw to it that every McCormick machine was built in his own factory. There he could dominate and so be assured that his experience-bred demands for high quality would be met.

If the 1831 reaper was but a crude affair compared with his later models, the first Chicago shop was no more than a pale foreshadowing of the factories he was later to organize. But as the original reaper won the plaudits of the observers who watched it, so the factory of 1848 was remarkable in the eyes of those who saw in it the beginning of Chicago's industry. A reporter for a Chicago paper wrote of the little shop:

It is situated on the north side of the river near the piers [it stood some three hundred feet east of the north end of the present Michigan Avenue Bridge] and is a well-finished brick building, 100 feet by 30 or over and three stories high. Attached to the main building is a building containing a steam engine, lathes for turning iron, and also a building containing six forges. There are 33 hands employed in the factory, ten of whom are blacksmiths.... The engine drives some fourteen or fifteen machines; viz. a planing machine, two circular saws, a tenent saw, a lathe for turning handles for rakes, pitchforks, etc.; also two lathes for turning iron, a gage's patent die, two morticing machines and two grindstones. Machines are being set up for various other uses in several branches of carpenter's work.... We understand the proprietors design enlarging [the smithy] as it is at present too contracted for the wants of the factory.

A wood reaper hewn out by 'machines for various other uses in several branches of carpenter's work' has become a steel machine speeding along behind a tractor: the thirty-three 'hands' have become six thousand workmen: the little steam engine that was the pride of young Chicago is now a humming electric generator: the fifteen machine tools have become eleven thousand. Yes, McCormick Works has grown!

The growth began immediately. By the end of 1849

THE FIRST McCORMICK REAPER FACTORY, ON THE CHICAGO RIVER

As it appeared before the Fire of 1871

the main building had been extended to a length of one hundred and ninety feet. There were three planing machines, six saws, nine lathes, three boring machines, and sixteen forges. A hundred and twenty men were at work. There were riverside docks for unloading materials from lake schooners and for shipping finished reapers. In 1851, a fire destroyed a large part of the old main building and a new four-story wing was erected. Machinery 'of the latest design' was installed. After the reconstruction, a reporter of the *Chicago Daily Journal* visited the factory and wrote an article on 'The Magic of Machinery,' which I quote from Professor Hutchinson's account of those early days:

An angry whirr, a dronish hum, a prolonged whistle, a shrill buzz and a panting breath — such is the music of the place. You enter — little wheels of steel attached to horizontal, upright and oblique shafts, are on every hand. They seem motionless. Rude pieces of wood without form or comeliness are hourly approaching them upon little railways, as if drawn thither by some mysterious attraction. They touch them, and *presto*, grooved, scalloped, rounded, on they go, with a little help from an attendant, who seems to have an easy time of it, and transferred to another railway, when down comes a guillotine-like contrivance, — they are morticed, bored, and whirled away, where the tireless planes without hands, like a boatswain, whistle the rough plank into polish, and it is turned out smoothed, shaped, and fitted for its place in the Reaper or the Harvester. The saw and the cylinder are the genii of the establishment. They work its wonders and accomplish its drudgery. But there is a greater than they. Below, glistening like a knight in armor, the engine of forty-horse power works as silently as the 'little wheel' of the matron; but shafts plunge, cylinders revolve, bellows heave, iron is twisted into screws like wax, and saws dash off at the rate of forty rounds a second, at one movement of its mighty muscles. But there is a greater still than this. There by the furnace fire, begrimed with coal and dust, decorated with an apron of leather, instead of a ribbon of satin, stands the one who controls — nay, who can create the whole.

The factory beside the Chicago River kept on growing. In 1856, it had a producing capacity of forty reapers each day and actually made four thousand that year. In 1859, when it had passed its tenth birthday, there was a total floor area of 110,000 square feet. Leander J. McCormick, a younger brother of Cyrus, was the plant superintendent. There were four foremen of the wood, metal, foundry, and repair departments. Three hundred men worked a ten-hour day for a wage of from one dollar to two dollars per day. The manufacturing program for the season consumed 371,000 feet of lumber, 48,776 pounds of cast steel, 62,500 feet of iron chain, 661 tons of wrought iron, 942 tons of pig iron, 170,000 pounds of malleable iron finger guards, 90,000 pounds of tin, copper, and sheet zinc, and 437 tons of coal.

An industry of such scope would seem pathetically small to-day; but in its infant stature there lay the promise of gigantic proportions in the future. Also, compared with what had gone before, this factory was impressive.

Previous to this and other American factories, the world's sole effort at anything resembling industrialization lay with British spinners. In the eighteenth century, a home industry equipped with fireside looms had been suddenly, rudely, metamorphosed into a factory system by the invention of spinning-mill machinery. The picturesque inefficiency of high-cost hand looms gave place to squalid, crowded, degrading shops. Machine looms were necessary to progress, but progress was slowed by the turmoil caused by the oppression meted out by inexperienced capitalists to caste-ridden villagers viciously turned into slaves of the machine. Workingmen smashed the new labor-saving machinery. They thought their jobs were being destroyed. No one was wise enough as yet to realize that machinery would not only reduce cost, but actually mean more work and a greater purchasing power through widespread and higher wages. But no such economic cycle was ever heard of until within the years of American industrial progress. Even in this country no clear understanding of it has existed until the most recent quarter-century. It has been left for modern America to garner the economic fruits of true industrialism.

Industry began when some early man became so skilled at making stone axes or flint arrowheads that he undertook to produce them for his neighbors as well as for himself. As soon as his trade grew enough to warrant a helper, organization came into being. But there the growth of industry stopped. In all their experience, neither the luxurious Egyptians nor the wise Greeks nor the rich Romans nor the monks of the Middle Ages nor the princes of the Renaissance created out of their manner of living enough of a demand to bring more of a factory system into existence than the artisan and his own few apprentices.

As material production increased in response to an increasing population's demand for necessities and luxuries, certain men naturally acquired skill in making articles for sale. Their products were sought after for their intrinsic worth. They made the things that were asked for, and when a new demand came into being, they invented new articles. It must, for example, have created a stir in early military circles when some smith produced the earliest protective armor; and the carpenter who first devised a chair must have been famous. The theory of organization that accompanied primitive production did not advance until the Middle Ages, when trade guilds were devised to supplant the slavery of pagan days. But even when the discovery of new portions of the globe gave so great an impetus to human vision, business methods did not change greatly. The stock company was invented in the sixteenth century, thus permitting the ownership of commerce and industry to be diversified; yet the actual conduct of business went on pretty much as before so far as methods and management were concerned. Production still remained in the hands of a few skilled men who divided their time between work with their own hands and such instruction as they provided for student apprentices. These last were learning to acquire the art of their trade and would become the artisans of the future.

It was the individualism fostered by the guild system that caused ancient production to be so very worth while in its results. Benvenuto Cellini may be an outstanding example of the ability of labor to produce beauty, but there were countless other men in whom stirred the spirit of creativeness. A master workman acquired a reputation for excellence; apprentices were drawn to him by his fame in his profession; they grew up in the tradition of his skill; and, as invariably happens, the quality of one effort was improved when intelligence carried it on into the next. An apprentice toiling to chisel out a silver goblet or weave velvet or carve a piece of fine furniture could see his work develop from day to day. It was necessary for him to understand what results he was trying to accomplish and to believe in his work. He could scan in his own hands the whole progression of manufacture and therein could control his own career. He developed as his work advanced. It is not necessary to assume that every product of such a system of business was beautiful or that every worker was endowed with outstanding ability. Men were probably pretty much of an average then as now — some good, some medium, some bad. The truth was that the old guild system allowed such brains as men possessed to develop in the most individual manner. The surprising thing is that this individualism did not produce more inventions.

That it failed to do so was due to the conditions of life rather than to the state of business organization. Even a method that allowed workmen to become artists could not cause them to develop beyond surrounding circumstances. The horizon of fifteenth-century Europe hardly overpassed the two ends of the Mediterranean. As soon as the Western Hemisphere was discovered and a road was found to the East Indies, men's imaginations flared. Yet even when young America was brought into being, the older commercial methods remained in force. One thing alone brought about a change: the inventions which were the birth of modernism in industry.

I do not assert that factories in 1850 were more than the seed from which modern American business has grown. But I see in them all, and in Cyrus Hall McCormick's reaper factory in particular, the root of what we do to-day. Later I shall have more to say of present-day production. For the present, let it be assumed that the American manufacturing system depends, among other things, upon standardization and mass production. Mass production includes the ordered progress of a part in process of manufacture from the raw material stage through one machining operation after another and so into the various steps of assembly. These two elements of mass production were devised in Cyrus Hall McCormick's factory just as surely as he invented and produced the first reaper.

Consider what the *Chicago Journal* reporter observed in 1851. He wrote of materials approaching their destination on 'little railways,' apparently on a definite schedule; of transfer mechanism to handle material from one conveyor system to another; and of the ordered succession of woodworking operations. Each of these statements is an indication of rudimentary mass production. Furthermore, this journalist of long ago stated that the attendant seemed to be having 'an easy time of it.' This effortless type of man-labor is the very essence of mass production, where tireless mechanism substitutes for the heavy work that used to make a man strain at his toil. Mass production depends much on mind and little on muscle, and it would seem that this fact had been discovered by the inventor of the reaper. In subsequent years many special machine tools were devised in his enlarged Chicago factories, all designed to reduce production cost to a minimum. Doubtless his employees and not he himself conceived them. He inspired them.

As for standardization of parts, a *Chicago Tribune* reporter wrote in 1859, 'A farmer of Illinois or Missouri who, in an earlier year bought a machine, has only to mention the part he wishes duplicated, with the year of his purchase, and from the "Repair Room" the pattern-maker or the foundryman takes his pattern and fills the order promptly.' This quotation teaches an interesting lesson on the function of rendering service which now, seventy years later, is so proudly stressed in the advertising of every company that sells a mechanical product to the public. It also suggests that in the early McCormick Reaper Works there was an acute understanding of the interchangeability of parts, which is popularly supposed to have originated among the makers of automobiles.

There seems to be one way only of accounting for McCormick's mastery over manufacturing problems. His commercial mentality, originally mechanical, had to clothe itself with a salesman's enthusiasms. But before selling, he had to conquer an entirely undeveloped field of manufacturing endeavor and pioneer a way toward modern production methods. He did so because of his unbending insistence upon that dearest ally of a salesman — quality. He preached quality to his factory men until it was engraved on their hearts. In modern parlance, he 'sold' them quality so well that they understood the necessity for it and therefore believed in it. Each year the McCormick reaper became heavier, stronger, better: each year it gained more favor with the farmers. My father has told me how he used to hear his father say, 'I don't want to make my entire profit from a single sale — I want to make the machines so good that the farmer and his sons will come back again and again to buy more McCormick machines.' A common statement among salesmen was, 'This reaper is so strong that you can hitch your team to it, go anywhere the Lord permits, and the machine will do its work.'

The most spectacular part of modern industry is its manufacturing efficiency. The science that underlies mass production has grown from such small beginnings as McCormick's factory on the Chicago River, with its five stories and its three hundred men, until now it is the familiar genius of those who would produce their thousands of articles per day. But manufacturing skill is not the whole of industry. Even in his earliest days in Virginia, Cyrus Hall McCormick was exploring other foundations of modern business.

The first advertisement of the reaper appeared in 1833 in the *Lexington Union*. From time to time until 1835.

McCormick published notices of it and also of his hillside plow. These early documents are interesting merely as indicating that the system of advertising and propaganda he devised after his move to Chicago had a contemporary root in the mental energy and imaginative vision that produced the reaper. Once he had invented his machine, he was foreordained to forge ahead to its manufacture. The business which he was to develop was to be a well-rounded whole, to include both the reaper and the genesis of the organization methods which to-day's generation uses.

After 1840, McCormick and his machine were naturally of much concern to the press of Virginia. By 1845, he was publishing long advertisements in the farm papers of Chicago, Detroit, Columbus, and northern New York. As his interest in the West increased and he began to withdraw his activities from the Atlantic seaboard, the Virginia newspapers turned their attention to Hussey. But, though he lost their praise, McCormick knew his destiny was bound up with the prairies.

The reaper advertisements of the middle century now seem naïve in the extreme, but that is only because we of this generation are accustomed to see our publicity couched in the modern style. In May, 1849, for example, McCormick, Ogden & Company published a handbill with a picture of a team of sleek horses at the top trotting along with a reaper in tow. A blithe boy cracks a whip, a waistcoated gentleworker in a top hat leans forward gracefully in his seat and rakes the severed grain from the platform. The text speaks of abundant crops to come, the labor shortage due to emigration to California, and the need of placing an early order before the supply should be exhausted. The reaper is 'now believed to be complete and unexceptionable in construction and cer-

A McCORMICK ADVERTISEMENT OF 1849

tain to give still greater satisfaction to all in their operation than ever before.' A list of reaper agents is added.
The lower half of the circular is filled with an elabo-
rately worded round-robin testimonial of satisfactory
mechanical and money-saving performance signed by
farmers throughout Indiana, Illinois, Wisconsin, and
Iowa.

If any one questions why I see in such an advertisement, spread abroad in a world that knew so little of
organized publicity, the genesis of modern advertising,
let him consider a moment: The reaper and its trotting
team are a small automobile made to seem large by a
draftsman's art; the smiling boy and the raker with
his top hat are the modishly dressed family group out
for a self-satisfied motor airing; the prediction of farm
prosperity is the same as that urge to buy which makes us
want refrigerators and radios and encyclopædias; the
mechanical perfection of the reaper is similar to the last
word of style or design that compels us to buy Blank's
product, whatever it may be. The farmers' testimonials
are the 1849 model of a society leader's purchased assurance that her complexion could not survive without such
and such soap. And as for simplicity — why, 'the Machines will all be so numbered and marked with paint,
showing the connection of the different parts one with
another that they can readily be put together by the
farmer.'

McCormick added one element to his advertising campaign which is indicative of the fine assurance with which
he regarded his own work. As early as 1842, when for the
first time he began to be really satisfied with his invention, he gave his customers an absolute guaranty of satisfactory performance or the return of their money. Obviously the satisfaction must be measured in terms of that

day, not of this. The performance of the early reaper was in harmony, not with the twentieth-century usage, but with the untrained wants of the farmers of former days. Farmers now are more experienced and want more. But the reapers of that day suited that day's farmers, and they suited the pride of Cyrus Hall McCormick. In 1852, he published this grand challenge to the world: 'I warrant them superior to Hussey's and to all others. I have a reputation to maintain. Let a farmer take both and keep the one which he likes best.' What has the twentieth century added to such confidence in the high quality of the service your product is ready to perform?

Field tests of competitive reapers were continually organized. It will be remembered how McCormick ordered his brothers to 'meet Hussey in Maryland and *put him down*.' The trials increased in number as more competitors came into the field; but, by the same token, the reliability of their results decreased. A poor patch of grain would defeat a worthy entrant, some one would appear with a specially built machine, a local gladiator would win favor with the local judges. There was a six-day test at Geneva, New York, in 1852, when Burrall's reaper and Manny's mower won. Densmore's reaper and Ketchum's mower carried off the honors at Springfield, Ohio. There followed a war of letters led by McCormick. He and his rivals occupied columns of newspaper space. He proved by statistics that he should have won and issued ringing challenges for next year's harvest. It is perhaps significant that he went on selling as many machines as all of his competitors together.

There was nothing of the subtlety of modern advertising in these documents proclaiming the relative merits of the early machines; and one can hardly call the style of the long letters in the press restrained. Competitors hit straight from the shoulder, they damned each other without mercy, they called Heaven to witness their own perfection. They spoke the florid language of the day — the same language which, in the Nation's young diplomatic correspondence, caused so many sneers among the chancelleries of polished Europe and produced such unequivocal results. America was growing up. America was inventing things of which Europe had never dreamed. Americans liked an amusing controversy. The reaper polemics appealed to their native humor. They clamored for more debate — and the publicity paid. McCormick led all the others in pungent argument. Advertising, like the reaper, was developing under the touch of his creative hands.

Advertising pronunciamentos and lengthy disputes in the columns of the papers were meat and drink to the inventor-turned-business-man. He loved to debate and he never wearied of extolling the merits of his reaper. Writing of this kind he could do himself; but, as soon as the production of the Chicago factory became impressive, he could no longer travel through the country as had been his wont, pockets full of order blanks and handbills, and himself take orders. The volume of his business was now enough to require executive attention. McCormick and his brothers had time to do no more than take an occasional trip through the wheat lands, excursions which served as a vacation to country-bred men tied by force of circumstances to an office. They perforce appointed deputies to do the actual selling.

The first official traveling representative was a cousin, J. B. McCormick, who after 1845 roved up and down the lower Ohio valley and into Tennessee and Missouri. In 1848, the first regular 'traveling agents' were appointed as territorial supervisors. H. G. Hubbard, A. G. Hager, and J. L. Wilson were the earliest forerunners of the great army of traveling implement salesmen who now encircle the globe. The main function of these pioneers was to represent the home office in appointing and supervising the local agents who were the direct approach to the farming public.

The duties of the local agents were not very different from what they are to-day. Their contract provided that they should maintain a sample machine, canvass the wheat districts in the territory assigned to them, deliver reapers and instruct purchasers in their operation, stock spare parts, be prepared to do repair work and render field service, make reports, collect money due on notes, and distribute advertising. They often operated through sub-agents, country blacksmiths or general storekeepers, who may perhaps be considered the first farm implement retailers. Rules of procedure were laid down for them, but these they broke with impunity if by so doing they could advance the McCormick cause. They were supplied with sales arguments for their own machine and against rivals, but when they were face to face with the fact of competition, they had to rely mainly on their own initiative and energy. The report of one of them, which I quote from Hutchinson's biography, gives such a delightful picture of the sterling days of old that I repeat it at length:

I found in the neighborhood supplied from Cassville quite early in the season one of Manny's agents with a fancyfully painted machine cutting the old prairie grass to the no small delight of the witnesses, making sweeping and bold declarations about what his machine could do and how it could beat yours, etc., etc. Well, he had the start of me, I must head him somehow. I began by breaking down on his fancy machine pointed out every objection that I could see and all that I had learned last year... gave the statements of those that had seen the one work in my grass... all of which I could prove. And then stated to all my opinion of what would be the result should they purchase from Manny. You pay one half money and give your note for the balance, are prosecuted for the last note and the cheapest way to get out of the scrape is to pay the note, keep the poor machine and in a short time purchase one from McCormick... Now gentlemen I am an old settler, have shared all the hardships of this new country with you, have taken it Rough and Smooth... have often been imposed on in the way I allmost know you would be by purchasing the machine offered you to-day. I would say to all, try your machine before you [pay] one half or any except the freight. I can offer you one on such terms, warrant it against this machine or any other you can produce, and if after a fair trial... any other proves superior and you prefer it to mine, keep [it]. I will take mine back, say not a word, refund the freight, all is right again. No Gentlemen this man dare not do this.

The Result you have seen. He sold not one. I sold 20. About the same circumstances occurred in Lafayette County.

All Harvester dealers the world over know men like this D. R. Burt, of Waterloo, Iowa. He was as much a fighting pioneer as was his chief, he knew the toil of service and the challenge of success, he saw clearly his single objective in life and he gained it. The agents of seventy-five years later are no less hardy, no less fine, no less devoted to the higher destiny of the country Burt was helping to make. But they do not knife competitors. The world is more graceful now than then, that is all. Burt is gone and the men like him, but similar trials remain. There is a motor-car to ride instead of a horse, there are leagues to journey instead of miles, there are many machines to tend instead of a few — but the farmer, a newer and wiser farmer, is still asking to be served.

Each year the reaper was better, but there were, nevertheless, many complaints for the agent to adjust. The gearing on the 1853 reapers failed and had to be replaced during the following winter, free of cost to the purchasers.

Farmers would insist on delaying their orders until late, hail might come to ruin an assured crop, pests would ravage a harvest and change triumph into disaster, machinery was not understood, reapers needing repair were left standing in the field through the winter and given no attention until the last frantic moment before harvest. A factory expert sent out from Chicago to help an agent reported: 'I am sorry I enlisted, but there is no use, I shall go through with the Job if I live — the machines are in the worst plight imaginable. I have found them outdoors and frozen down just where they used them last.'

The most important innovation introduced into his selling system by McCormick was his plan of credit and easy terms. From the very beginning of his career, he recognized that a farmer's ability to buy was different from that of other men. By the very nature of his business, a farmer cannot keep on hand a large supply of liquid capital. This may not have mattered much when each agriculturist produced his own food and clothing; but things changed as soon as there were manufactured articles to be bought and paid for. A wheat farmer's income comes in once a year, after harvest, and he must pay for the machine he uses out of the receipts he gathers after the machine has done its work. McCormick himself said that one could sell a reaper only by waiting until it had paid for itself.

In the early fifties the price of a reaper was $125. The farmer was asked to pay $35 cash plus the freight from Chicago. The balance was due on December 1st, with 6 per cent interest from July 1st. However much the local agents were instructed to adhere to these terms, it is certain they never hesitated to depart from them. In practice the cash received at the time of a sale varied from ten per cent to twenty-five per cent, and the balance was collected whenever possible within the next year and a half.

Of course such a credit system entailed some losses. To-day, farm credit is generally considered the best in the world. In the days when the West was being settled, men were often cruelly tested in their battle with the soil and many failed. Credit losses were therefore higher than now, and varied from three to five per cent. The cost of collections is given as seven and one-half per cent. In 1856, for example, only a third of the business done was for cash and the collectible portion of the balance was secured within fourteen months. Such extended credit demanded a huge provision of capital and could have been justified only by what would now be considered colossal profits.

The subsequent history of credits to farmers has followed accepted economic law. As the risk decreased, the necessity for such large profits diminished; as the volume rose, the profit per sale lessened. Farm credits have since become more secure. That they were good even in McCormick's later days is indicated by a story of the weeks immediately succeeding the Chicago Fire. He sat on a bank directorate with the great merchant, Marshall Field. The latter, whose business had been all but obliterated by the conflagration, therefore had an opportunity to see how money was rolling into McCormick's account from the country. Field sought and obtained a loan of one hundred thousand dollars, which money became the foundation of his reconstituted business.

There is a story current among the older men of the International Harvester Company which illustrates Cyrus Hall McCormick's attitude toward the pioneers of farming in the West and their crying need for credit. In the early days, when most of the country was unculti-

Property of
Bethany College
Library

vated, farming was a precarious venture, and outpost
farmers, who had bought reapers on time, would too frequently lose their grain and have no income. McCormick
met such a situation at Webster City, Iowa, then a mere
dot on the broad prairies. When he heard of their crop
failure and their inability to meet their notes, he shook
hands with each one of the worried debtors, promised to
see them through, won their friendship to such an extent
that for years none but a McCormick machine could be
sold in the town — and never lost a penny.

By 1856, there were McCormick agents all over the
wheat-growing sections of the United States. They were
putting into effect the sales portion of a new business
system. Cyrus Hall McCormick had invented a reaper
for a world that needed mechanized farming. When that
was done, he had provided as a background for his machine a new kind of factory, where, though he doubtless
knew it not, he was developing the first steps toward
standardization and mass production. Then he invented
a system of distribution which included the first bold use
of public debate in the press to expound his new mechanical doctrine, the first broad warranty of a manufactured product, the first aggressive system of selling, the
first conception of service, and the first broad application
of credit. He invented the reaper, and he also invented
the means to make it attainably useful to farmers.

It is possible that future historians will allot as important a place to the second feat as to the invention of
the reaper. McCormick's was the first successful machine
of its kind. Too many inventions which might otherwise
be of use to the world fail because the element of commercial appreciation is not added to them, or because
the cost of production is too high, or because no adequate distribution system is matured. The inventor of

the reaper provided the needed accessories to supply his device to the world. He projected the entire distributing plan himself and, to care for production, he developed around him a circle of able men, whose work adds to rather than detracts from his fame. He himself, a farmer turned inventor and forced by circumstances to develop new business methods, was the organizer who metamorphosed his visions into a practical and integrated unit of service to agriculture.

CHAPTER IV

THE EVOLUTION OF THE INDUSTRY

As ONE reviews the life record of Cyrus Hall McCormick, one is constantly impressed with the fine results arising from the interplay of his vigor and his imagination. While he does not appear consciously to have set about to guide destiny, some subtle force seems ever to have been piloting him and insuring his progress. Once his eyes were fixed upon an objective, however distant, nothing short of complete attainment satisfied him. Thus, he discovered foreign trade, fought for and captured a full share of it, and, in a day when the United States was an importing country, strove mightily beside those who turned the balance of trade in our favor. Having invented first the reaper and then a business, a part of the latter task was his foresensing of the fact that much of our national commercial destiny might lie overseas. Other men's eyes were fixed on the West, whose worth he appreciated as much as any one. His processes of thought were so rapid that he was able to comprehend the tremendous nature of that problem and still have room for Europe within the range of his vision.

During the years when his every energy might be thought to have been devoted to the new factory in Chicago and to the development of the Western States, he had time to note and understand the significance of the fact that the exportation of wheat from the United States to Europe was increasing. Perhaps the chief cause of this was the growth of inland railway transportation; but the reaper also was playing an important part in transforming America into a food-exporting country. In Great Britain, the cradle was less widely used than in America and the starvation wages paid to farm labor had driven harvesters to the cities to seek work or to California to find gold; so the stage was undoubtedly set for machinery. Indeed, Englishmen had long been striving to solve the problem of the reaper, but neither Ogle nor Bell nor any other had approached success.

Ever since 1849, when he built a special machine designed for presentation to Prince Albert's Royal Agricultural Society, McCormick had been turning his eyes toward the English market. The Crystal Palace Exhibition of the Industries of All Nations in the summer of 1851 furnished the suitable occasion. He sent the special reaper across the Atlantic in the spring and himself followed in August. Hussey had heard of his rival's plans and sent a machine of his own. They met before two hundred spectators including the jury from the Exhibition and Hussey's machine failed miserably because of the operator's lack of skill. A second trial confirmed the result of the first, and the Virginia reaper was awarded the Council Medal, the highest prize of the Fair.

Before this test the reaper — and, indeed, the entire American exhibit — had been made the butt of criticism and newspaper sarcasm. The young United States had developed little art of its own, so it could show nothing except those useful products it had provided to make its own daily life more tolerable. Cotton, tobacco, india-rubber shoes, a new repeating pistol, and articles for household use were shown. McCormick's reaper, perhaps because of the prominence of the stand it occupied, drew upon itself the special ire of the London *Times*. 'It is a cross between an Astley Chariot, a wheelbarrow, and a flying machine,' said The Thunderer; and it went on to sneer that America was 'proud of her agricultural implements which [English manufacturers] would reject as worthless.' But by the time the Exhibition was over the American exhibits had won more prizes in proportion than the British themselves. The McCormick reaper was attracting more attention than the Kohinoor diamond and the *Times* declared that it might repay Great Britain for the entire cost of the Exhibition.

McCormick made arrangements with a British firm to manufacture his reaper and went home. Hussey remained behind and, under his own skilled handling, won two subsequent field trials from the Virginia machine. For some time both reapers continued popular in England and both were sold in considerable numbers with far less resistance than they had met ten years previously in America. But by 1855 the tide of popular favor turned to McCormick.

However much England progressed in mechanized harvesting, France remained true to hand methods until 1855, when there was an International Exposition in Paris. A great field trial for reapers was organized, the McCormick machine won and was given the Grand Medal of Honor. Horace Greeley, who had also witnessed the American triumph at the Crystal Palace, wrote to the *New York Tribune* that the reaper's victory was 'more beneficent and creditable for the United States than if fifty thousand of her troops had defeated one hundred thousand choice European soldiers.'

The reaper was spreading rapidly throughout Europe. A McCormick machine was sold in Austria in 1849, and the Austrian press looked forward to the day when American machinery would solve the labor problem in Austria and counteract the drift of the peasants toward rebellion. A few years later, the reaper was introduced into Prussia and Poland. In 1858, the first McCormick machine reached Russia. At every opportunity the reaper was exhibited at the great international fairs and carried off many prizes to bring credit to itself and honor to its inventor. During the inventor's lifetime it won ten major and many hundred minor awards, far more than any of its competitors. Cyrus Hall McCormick was himself made a corresponding member of the Legion of Honor and a member of the Institute of France for having done more than any living man for the cause of agriculture.

One great advantage to the American manufacturers, who were thus picturesquely and successfully struggling to expand their trade into foreign lands, was the advertising value they saw in the reports they were able to publish at home of their foreign triumphs. Such reports opened the eyes of American farmers to the honor accorded their native machinery by old and instructed Europe. There lay the seat of all wisdom, all experience. Our country was brave and confident, but it lacked sure knowledge based on precedents of its own; so a reaper salesman was helped when he could say that the selfsame product he was selling west of the Mississippi was operating on the royal farms of France and England. Even yet American farmers were asking for proof before they bought — or perhaps it would be more accurate to say that they were evincing an increasing interest in quality.

At the moment of its birth, the reaper was by no means perfect. It contained in its design the seven vital principles without which grain cannot be harvested at all, but it cut grain precariously. In its first years its commercial value was hampered by its mechanical insufficiency. Then came the initial conception of the properly arranged and opposed cutter-bar serrations, the first of McCormick's post-invention period improvements, which were to make the original device entirely practicable. The addition of a seat for the raker made the machine easier to operate. After the move to Chicago, changes to facilitate operation, increase durability, and expand its usefulness were many. Even before the reaper was turned into the binder, these improvements were fundamental. They were betterments added to the seven original principles, and, since no one of them vitiated the 1831 elements, they strengthened them.

After 1848, the home office was kept in touch with the performance of the reapers in the field principally by the reports of agents and the analyses of complaints sent in by the company's own travelers. McCormick himself had to spend long periods in Europe, where his business was expanding hugely. His correspondence frequently expresses the despair he felt at being so far from the prairie farms he loved. But he had left behind him, graven in the minds of the men in charge of his business, a solemn command to keep the reaper abreast of any demand for betterment.

So, as the agents reported trouble due to poor design or too frequent breakage of a part, the reaper was strengthened or improved. Before 1855, the weight of the machine had increased from eight hundred to twelve hundred pounds. The main wheel was enlarged to effect better riding qualities and a steadier drive for the mechanism. The reel was again improved. The wood platform was covered with sheet zinc to make it more durable and the grain easier to rake off. A seat was provided on the machine for the driver as well as for the raker. Malleable iron guards were substituted for cast iron as soon as a dependable source of supply could be found. Most important of all, the modern form of knife with riveted-on cutting sections was devised in 1851. These sections were triangular pieces of steel with serrations cut in their diagonal edges. Thus the former straight cutter bar, with opposed serrations incised into its forward edge, now became nothing more than a carrying member, and the actual attack on the grain was made by the sections.

All reaper inventors started out with the theory that a reaper designed to harvest grain would also cut grass. In the middle forties it began to appear that this hope would not be realized. Certain reapers developed in grass districts were unsuccessful in grain; certain reapers, such as McCormick's, whose main objective was grain, were inferior as mowers. Men began to understand that the two problems were different. Wheat or oats, when ready for harvest, present a dry, brittle stalk which is easily severed by a sharp knife. Green grass is tougher by far. Furthermore, it is desirable to cut grass closer to the ground than is necessary with wheat. The guards of a mower cutter bar almost scrape the ground, and stones which would be overpassed by a grain reaper will wedge between the projecting fingers of mower guards. Grass has more of a tendency to drag or clog in the space between the cutting knife and the guards; hence the angularity of the cutting members must be different in a mower.

For such reasons, the early attempts to perform both functions with the same mechanism were doomed to failure. Hence the effort McCormick and others made to develop a combined type of reaper which could be turned into a mower simply by removing one cutter bar and substituting another. The first McCormick mower was a reaper with the platform removed. When it was tried in prairie grass near Chicago in 1849, it was even equipped with the reel. It did not perform at all; so next year a mower attachment with a new knife was produced. Even this got nowhere until, in 1851, the iron cutter bar with the riveted-on sections was developed and special mower guards were invented. However great its success in grain, the McCormick reaper could not be called a good mower, at least in its earlier years.

In the meantime other men were achieving distinction in the mower field. Hussey's reaper, though never a great commercial success, was a better grass machine than McCormick's. In later years the old sailor won a suit for patent infringement against his ancient rival and collected a large sum in damages. William F. Ketchum became for a time the country's leading mower exponent. He gave over the attempt to build a combined mower and reaper; and it is probable that his concentration on a single purpose was beneficial. Manny had the best combination mower and reaper. McCormick's adaptation of his reaper was inferior to several of his competitors' machines; but all were outdistanced in 1858 when Lewis Miller invented the famous Buckeye mower, a two-wheel machine with a hinged cutter bar. In that day of strife between competitors and constant friction, it is interesting to note that in 1860 the Buckeye consolidated with its two chief independent rivals and thus effected the world's first agricultural implement combination. McCormick forged on alone, ahead of all others because he had at his back the best business organization.

He was never of a coöperative frame of mind so far as his competitors were concerned. The temper of the times was entirely individualistic and he was one of the men who set the fashion of thought for his day. Like many another born leader, he found it impossible to subordinate the force of his will to any thought of compromise or collective action. He was strong enough to carry on alone, he was sure of his cause and of himself: why should he not fight for his rights and himself defend them when they were won? If he failed, no one would help him. The business captains of early American industry had to be hardy warriors or they fell.

Thus, when McCormick returned from England in 1851, it was to meet Seymour and Morgan in the courts. Ever since the Brockport partners had started to put on the market a renamed copy of the Virginia Reaper, much bad blood had naturally existed. Charges were hurled through the press, threats were exchanged, and at last McCormick sued. His rivals made some changes and gave their machine a new name; he won in the lower court, and the issue dragged along until 1854 when he was awarded $9,354 damages. The interesting point is not that Seymour and Morgan were thus driven from the reaper field — their competition was never very important after 1853 except in New York — but that McCormick so boldly assumed a front-line position against his competitors in what has been called the 'battle of the reapers.'

The long war with John H. Manny, the most brilliant and successful of all his competitors, followed immediately. McCormick filed suit against him for infringement of the minor 1845 and 1847 patents. Practically all other reaper manufacturers went in self-protection to the aid of Manny. To make a very long story short, the verdict sustained Manny, complimented McCormick, and was immediately appealed to the Supreme Court. There also, in 1858, Manny's innocence was reaffirmed; but he himself had died in the meantime. At the height of his career, his sale of machines exceeded all other competitors and equaled McCormick's. He was another of those brilliant American farmer boys who wrought so ably in the embattled field of young business.

The vital interest to-day in this suit is in the array of legal talent employed. McCormick's case was argued by a corps of able patent attorneys. Manny's counsel included, among others, Edwin M. Stanton, who was soon to become Secretary of War, and a comparatively unknown young man by the name of Abraham Lincoln. What might otherwise have been little more than a patent quarrel of local significance thus took on national importance. It was Lincoln's first big case; he earned for the first time a thousand-dollar fee; and the oratory of Stanton fired his enthusiasm and inspired him toward the Lincoln-Douglas debates which paved his way to the Presidency.

McCormick's complete defeat left him apparently as weak as he had seemed when Congress refused to extend either his original or his subsequent patents. But in reality he was so strongly entrenched that he needed no patents. The technical advantages of his enemies could not tear down the commercial ramparts he had built with his executive ability and strengthened with the enormous farmer goodwill he possessed. His brother William was right when he told Cyrus that his success was due not to patents but to his ability to make and sell machines.

Cyrus Hall McCormick's biographer has this to say about his career during these eventful times: he 'never appears to better advantage than during the years after 1848. He doubled and quadrupled his sales, greatly enlarged his factory, dispensed with partners, fought his rivals in Congress and in the courts, abroad and at home, on countless harvest fields. He was admired and hated, fawned upon and eulogized. But he never aroused sympathy for himself and probably would have spurned the man who offered it.' He was a militant Scotch-Irish pioneer, fired by the righteous zeal of his cause, forging forward with unconquerable will, unswerving in his purpose to serve the farmer.

The Civil War furnished the supreme test of the worth

of the reaper. The Commissioner of Agriculture said in 1862 that it would have been impossible to harvest the wheat crop if it had not been for the reapers in use in the West, each of which released five men for service in the army. The *Scientific American* published the statement that without 'horse-rakes, mowers and reaping machines, one half of the crop would have been left standing on the fields' Secretary Stanton, now McCormick's friend and ally, spoke glowing words of praise: 'The reaper is to the North what slavery is to the South. By taking the place of regiments of young men in the western harvest fields, it releases them to do battle for the Union at the front and at the same time keeps up the supply of bread for the Nation and the Nation's armies. Thus without McCormick's invention, I fear the North could not win and the Union would be dismembered.'

We who can look back on that tragic epoch know that the North won because of superior material resources: more factories, more munitions, more railways to gather together the offerings of a continent, more food. The reaper made the food possible. Food held Europe neutral when its sympathies were with the cotton-producing South. The reaper preceded the railways into the prairies and, in the hands of fighting frontiersmen, turned buffalo ranges into stands of wheat — made traffic to justify the building of the railways. The reaper brought the assurance of bread to the munition-making cities, and, because Europe had to have wheat, brought money back to the cities in return for the export of grain. The reaper did its share in making the United States and holding it secure.

The *post-bellum* reaper that followed the legions of discharged soldiers across the Missouri River or westward along the line of the Union Pacific Railway was no longer the reaper of the old days. Always McCormick was seeking to better it, and year by year he added whatever he thought would improve its operation. Obviously an automatic raking device would help. Many men had for long been trying to build a self-rake reaper and invariably they tried to sell their ideas to him; but he was never satisfied. One Jearum Atkins actually for a year or two bade fair to run away with the reaper trade; but his fantastic 'Iron Man' machine vanished after the panic of 1857. McCormick stood his ground and refused to desert his original type of reaper until something better appeared. His own self-rake machine was produced in 1862. This was the regular reaper equipped with a counterbalanced rake arm pivoting at the axis of the reel, which swept grain off the platform and to the side of the machine. It eliminated a man's labor and it was popular in its day. Yet it was but a step in the onward march toward the binder and cannot be said to have been epochal in any sense. It was a temporary convenience, not a startling invention like the original reaper, not a brilliant innovation like the harvester, nor a conclusive answer to a demand like the binder.

Enough has been said of other men who made and sold agricultural machinery before 1870 to indicate that, however outstanding Cyrus Hall McCormick may have been in the industry, he was by no means alone. He was the unquestioned leader, but he was never without competitors. Scores of companies were making reapers. Talcott and Emerson were carrying on the Manny tradition at Rockford. Benjamin H. Warder was producing reapers at Springfield in a partnership that was soon to include young J. J. Glessner. At Auburn, D. M. Osborne made the mowers that bore his name. Each of the many companies had a strong local following, and, though

McCORMICK'S SELF-RAKE REAPER OF 1864
A mechanically operated arm swept the grain off the platform

A McCORMICK HARVESTER OF THE MARSH TYPE
Popular during the years 1875–1883

McCormick had perhaps half of the entire trade in the United States, his business was centered largely in the non-manufacturing wheat districts west of Chicago.

This account of the evolution of the agricultural implement industry would be incomplete if it included no reference to that other man who, next after McCormick alone, so wrought that the problems of the farmer were made lighter. The reaper is the progenitor of all those agricultural implements which run upon the ground to deal with grown crops. Before the dawn of history, man had invented the plow as a more efficient crooked stick to get down under the surface and loosen the soil. But there was nothing scientific, nothing modern in the ancient method of hacking earth into clods and clods into dust. A plow was still the crudest of implements until the old-fashioned iron machine was introduced. Such a device, however, will not clean itself in sticky land and farmers would not continue to accept it. As the middle-western part of the United States was settled in the third decade of the nineteenth century, the cleaning, or scouring, difficulty became insuperable. An iron plow would break sod well enough, but when the once-virgin soil had been worked a few years, the loam would cake, stick to the face of the plow, and clog the operation of the implement.

At this time there lived in Grand Detour, an Illinois hamlet, one John Deere, who had moved there from Vermont in 1837. A blacksmith by trade, he had added the repairing of iron plows to his other work. It was out of the comparative failure of these rude tools that he hit upon his great contribution to the science of farming, the steel plow. He obtained a piece of broken bandsaw blade; he whittled a log into the shape he desired for the mold-board and share of his plow; then he heated the piece of steel, shaped and hardened it over the pattern; and lastly, he added a wrought-iron landside. On its initial test, this, the world's first commercial steel plow, proved a complete success, and John Deere's name, though he knew it not, was written on the pages of history.

There is a close parallel between Deere's plow of 1837 and McCormick's reaper of 1831. Both men seemed to accomplish instant success, neither was satisfied with his first work, both sought constantly to improve their device, and each of them did far more than merely achieve his immediate object. McCormick cut grain successfully by mechanism for the first time and won undying fame — and he also developed the seven elements without which no mechanical reaper can function. Deere gave the steel plow to a needy world, a machine that would scour and plow cleanly; but he should be equally famous because he, first of all men, reduced to a science the shape of the moldboard. He taught plow builders the world over that good preparation of the soil is dependent not merely on cutting into the ground, but on turning the sod over in a predetermined manner dictated by the nature of the soil.

John Deere's steel plow was not the very first; but, like McCormick, he had organizing ability enough to build a great business. He, too, had many worthy competitors, two of whom deserve special mention. James Oliver started making plows at South Bend in 1853. Seeking also to provide a plow that would scour in all kinds of soil, he turned to the use of chilled metal. Of the discouragements that attended his experimental efforts at invention he said: 'Plow men who had spent years in experimenting and had abandoned the project of a complete chilled plow advised me not to undertake it. Those who had aided me with money and influence forsook me, and

I was classed with the fools who pursue the fallacy of perpetual motion. Although feeling keenly the cuts of former friends, I determined to succeed. Day and night for years I thought of nothing else and made everything bend to this one great object of my life....' The world knows what splendid work for farmers has grown out of Oliver's consecration. Is it too much to say that determination coupled with vision are the necessary concomitants of *any* invention?

William Parlin came from the East to Canton, Illinois, in 1840. Like Deere, he made plows by conforming saw blades to wooden moldboards. A few years later, William Orendorff became his partner. While the former worked in the little shop, the latter drove about central Illinois with wagons loaded with plows. Aggressive salesmanship was invariably rewarded in the land of agricultural opportunity, and the business grew. Other implements were added to the line until, in 1866, Orendorff picked up the invention of a Missouri blacksmith, the first lister. Corn joined wheat immediately as a crop suitable for Western methods of cultivation.

Nothing, not even the business of these manufacturers of plows, was able to challenge McCormick's lead in the implement field. But the old reaper had lived too long and its doom was spelled by the invention of the harvester by two farmer boys by the name of Marsh. Their first sales in 1863 followed trying years of experimentation. Their theory was that harvesting was made slow and difficult by the necessity of collecting and binding grain on the ground where it fell from the reaper platform. It is said that the brothers were nervous and highstrung and could not tolerate any delay at the time of harvest. So, by a feat of time-saving motion-study worthy of a twentieth-century manufacturer, they elaborated a plan of raising the grain by means of continuous canvas aprons from the reaper platform over the top of the main wheel, where it fell neatly on a table. Two men rode the machine, standing before this table on a footboard. They bound the grain as fast as it fell over to them and then tossed the bundles to the ground. They could bind speedily because they were able to stand erect at their task; they did not have to step and stoop along, scraping armsful of wheat together and halting to bind the sheaf. Their work was brought to them — the machine recognized the fact of their brains, not their puny muscles.

At the close of the Civil War, a new era of farm expansion began and the tremendous step ahead taken by the Marsh brothers came in the nick of time. The machine won immediate popularity. McCormick at first refused to yield, but the march of progress was too strong. Many of his competitors went to the wall or took out licenses to make the Marsh type of harvester. The record does not relate how McCormick's pride and his esteem for the reaper took the shock of the reaper's defeat. We may assume, however, that a man whose commercial judgment was so acute knew better than to cry over spilt milk. The supremacy of the old machine was over — the farmers wanted progress; so he, too, began to build harvesters.

Every one realized how greatly the problem of harvesting had been simplified by the new machine. The self-rake reaper had eliminated the raker, a clear gain in the labor cost of a bushel of wheat. The Marsh harvester cut the time of binding in two. But no one for a minute believed that the end of mechanical development was in sight. There was one S. D. Carpenter, a loquacious Wisconsin editor who was himself something of an inventor and who for years had been preaching the doctrine of mechanical binding. Influenced by his trenchant arguments, farm opinion held that somehow the harvester must be equipped with mechanism to tie the bundles of grain. Most inventions, if recognized at all, appear to the men of their time to be the last word; but the Marsh harvester — which was in every sense a great invention — was believed to be merely a brilliant advance step on the highway of progress.

In 1872, Charles B. Withington sought out McCormick and showed him a model of a wire binder. The reaper inventor immediately saw that here was a chance to regain whatever prestige he had lost in his own eyes. He had lost none in the mind of the public, for the McCormick manufacturing and selling system had been powerful enough to carry on with the harvester in place of the reaper; but he could not be satisfied until he had made yet another contribution of his own to the science of agricultural machinery. So he bought the Withington device, built a few machines experimentally, and in 1877 was ready to produce the wire binder in quantities.

Farmers took up the wire binder as avidly as they had the harvester. McCormick swept the field. Fifty thousand of the new machines were sold in the next few years. In every place where wheat was grown, one could see the arm of the Withington binder thrust its way over the stream of wheat, seize a bundle of grain, lock the wire about its middle, cut it loose, and toss it bound upon the stubble. Some farmers objected. They said that the wire broke off and pieces mingled with the straw to the detriment of their stock. But the economy of labor made possible by the binder was sufficient to answer all objections. Hand labor had now practically been eliminated. A child old enough to hold the reins of a team could reap and bind the crop. The wire binder, with two men to pick up and shock the sheaves, could harvest twelve or fourteen acres of grain a day.

McCormick's renewed supremacy was rudely challenged in the harvest of 1880. One E. H. Gammon, a former Methodist minister, had left the pulpit for more lucrative service in the West where he sold reapers and Marsh harvesters. He came ultimately to control the Marsh factory at Plano, a suburb of Chicago, and took as a silent partner a former fellow townsman from Maine, William Deering. Deering was a new type of man to the implement industry. He knew nothing about agriculture. He had gained a fortune in the dry-goods business. Beginning life in his father's woolen mills, he had worked his way upward through the hard school of commerce and administration. He was the first man to enter the implement industry who had not fought his way through the bitter struggles of mechanical invention and soul-testing competition. In 1873, Deering moved to Chicago. He, too, Maine merchant though he was, felt the lure of the West; and as his contribution to it he brought perseverance equal to that of any of the more experienced gladiators already in the arena, and a nicely balanced judgment of the characters of men that matched his great commercial ability.

In 1879, Gammon fell ill and retired, and Deering, now in sole charge of the firm's affairs, decided to move away from Plano and build a new factory in Chicago's northern suburbs. At the same time he bought the ideas of John F. Appleby and prepared to build a twine binder. In the first season, 1880, he made and sold three thousand of the new machines. The wire binder's brief day of supremacy was over.

Appleby, one of the great names in the history of American invention, had hit upon the combination of

THE McCORMICK HARVESTER AND WIRE BINDER OF 1876
The first self-binder

ONE OF THE FIRST McCORMICK TWINE BINDERS
Built in 1881

successful units that had barred the access of all other men to the secret of a successful twine binder. He winnowed the wheat from the chaff of Locke's many inventions; from Carpenter he gathered the principle of the elevation and then the downward delivery of the stream of grain; from J. H. Gordon he got the idea of packer cranks to wedge the grain in front of the tying needle; from Behel he gleaned the idea for the knotter; and from Gorham he took the principle of the automatic trip to start the mechanism of the binder under the pressure of the weight of grain. He himself assimilated all the experience of previous twine-binder investigators, added his own genius, and continued the cycle begun by the invention of the reaper.

In one year Deering had built and occupied a new factory, bought a hitherto untried patent and turned it into an immensely successful machine, invaded a field already crowded with experienced manufacturers, and was rapidly running away with the remaining shreds of the popular favor they had gained through so many years! In truth, the age of romance was not yet over! There was still room in business for courage and resourcefulness and vigor and nerve and ability. The unostentatious, shrewd newcomer possessed them all.

Fifty years after the first test at Steele's Tavern, McCormick found his position again in jeopardy and his leadership challenged by competition far more serious than the Marsh harvester of a few years before. With extraordinary rapidity he adapted himself to the new circumstances, arranged for a license to manufacture the Appleby type of twine binder, and entered the 1881 harvest ready to do battle as before, valiantly, mightily, victoriously.

The evolution of the reaper was not complete until the

time when, decades later, the tractor would come into
being to furnish another type of motive power and demand other types of machinery. The reaper had lasted
for thirty years until it gave way to the self-rake reaper.
That yielded to the harvester, the parent of the binder.
The binder was to remain supreme for nearly forty years.
Its generation was to be a period of warfare and victory,
of commercial slaughter and increasing service, of bitter
hatred and the fineness of human vigor. McCormick's
career was to dominate the future, to guide the entire
half-century. His influence was to live on, even into the
age of power farming.

CHAPTER V

THE PIONEER

THE Chicago Fire of 1871 might have ruined the young metropolis if it had not been for the courage and the far-sightedness of a few leading men. When the holocaust was over, the entire business district of the city and a large part of the residential quarter had been wiped out. The fifteen thousand buildings which had occupied the district north of Harrison Street (where the present Harvester Building stands), south of Lincoln Park, and east of the two branches of the Chicago River, had been destroyed. Three and a half square miles of city and $188,000,000 worth of property were reduced to débris and ashes. Ninety-four thousand people were homeless and the working places of countless others had vanished.

Cyrus Hall McCormick's name figured prominently in the rebuilding of Chicago, for he was one of the group of leaders who had an aggressive confidence in the city's future. Time and romance have endowed these men with an aura of legend, attaching to their work for reconstruction a picturesqueness that is pleasant, but really less typical of them than the actual facts. Suffice it to say that in the minds of the captains of Chicago there was never any question of yielding.

McCormick's wife and children were at that time in Richfield Springs, New York. One morning they went placidly to the telegraph office to announce their intended departure for home. An excited clerk, hardly able to speak, refused to take Mrs. McCormick's message on the ground that there was no Chicago! That was not so, of course. Chicago's body had been destroyed, but its hard-

working, militant young spirit, as represented in the
brains and the enthusiasms of its better citizenry, was
very much alive. When some dispirited individuals began
to talk of moving to St. Louis or Milwaukee, the leaders
rose up and, by their force of will and courage, remade
the city.

W. D. Kerfoot built a shack in the middle of a former
downtown street and, announcing 'all gone but wife,
children, and energy,' went on selling real estate and
distributing enthusiasm. Mayor Roswell B. Mason built
a new city hall almost overnight. Joseph Medill, who
followed him in office, roused Chicago's enthusiasm for
sound construction. A rebuilt Board of Trade was opened
on the first anniversary of the fire. Field and Leiter lost
everything they possessed when their insurance companies failed, but they were smiling when their dry-goods
business opened temporarily in a stable. John V. Farwell
began to construct his new store while the stones of the
old buildings were still hot. Within two years Cyrus Hall
McCormick, Potter Palmer, R. T. Crane, and others
opened a huge exposition building on the lake front where
all the world might come and see how Chicago was
recovering from catastrophe.

McCormick met his wife five miles outside the ruined
city, gray from lack of sleep and with the arm of his coat
burned off. He drove with her to the wreck of the factory
to discuss the question of rebuilding. He was advancing
in years and was financially independent — he might
easily have accepted the destruction of his property as a
decree of fate and elected to live the remaining years of
his life at peace. But ease was not one of the things this
fighting pioneer was looking for. His was the restless
energy which was always seeking some service to perform.
He felt that the farmers of the world needed his machines.

And there was his constantly reiterated belief, 'I know of no better place for a man to die than in the harness.' In truth, he did not know how to give over striving.

There is a tale to the effect that McCormick left the decision to carry on or to retire to his wife; but to me it seems that his character would have made surrender impossible. He himself said, 'I at once determined to proceed with the work of rebuilding.' So temporary buildings were ordered while (as an octogenarian pensioner has told me) the workmen cheered.

Obviously the business had grown beyond the hemmed-in possibilities of the little factory. Ten thousand reapers had been sold that year and the early advent of the Marsh harvester would soon widen the demand for farm machinery. A few days before the fire, McCormick had acquired a new factory site on the southwest side of the city, far away from the crowded center of Chicago. To insure plenty of room for growth, he bought a wide expanse of prairie where his vacant acres might serve first as testing fields and then for the expanding industry he foresaw. If it did nothing else, the Chicago Fire hastened the construction of the new McCormick Works. The appliances which were the reaper's lineal descendants were bursting the seams of the garments cut so many years before to fit the frame of the reaper's youth. New pioneering was needed.

The first of the new buildings was a long four-story structure which housed the forge, the wood shop, and the machine and assembling departments. Behind it was the foundry. Seven hundred men worked in the factory for nine months of the year. During the harvest season it was customary to shut the plant down to permit the entire attention of the company to be given to the field. The first foundry has now given place to a towering manufacturing structure; but the four-story building still stands. High on its face is the proud legend of its past, 'McCormick Reaper Manufactory. Established 1831.' It is now too small for the giant production program of modern times, but, as a fitting tribute to McCormick's insistence on service to the farmer, it now houses the repairs department. And, as if in a memorial gesture of tribute to the founder of the industry, another sign repeats these words of a later president of the twentieth-century company, 'Quality is the foundation of our business.' The echo of the past is strong.

The new factory permitted the introduction of many manufacturing processes which are of the greatest interest to a student of the development of the American system of mass production. In certain cases their introduction took place after McCormick's death. Nevertheless, it seems to me that he was responsible for them as well as for the improvements which he directly supervised. Men can expect no greater tribute than to have their ideas carried forward by their successors into a generation energized, not by their presence, but by the unseen inspiration of their remembered greatness.

Huge warehouses were constructed where stocks of machines built during the winter could be accumulated against the invariably sudden shipping demand of the pre-harvest season. In 1875, a small locomotive was purchased to substitute more efficiently for horses, mules, or oxen in shunting railway cars to and from the various loading docks. The new gray iron foundry, which remained in service for twenty-five years until pulled down to make room for a larger building, had a capacity of a hundred tons of castings per day and was famous for its molding machinery and other time- and labor-saving equipment. Special boring machines were devised in

1886 to perform simultaneously several of the intricate operations leading to the completion of a mower frame. Painting tanks, where assembled units or even entire machines could be dipped into a pool of paint, were introduced in 1889 or earlier, and the slower method of applying color by means of hand brushing was abandoned.

Such methods are one and all fundamental to modern progressive manufacturing. The present system requires man-power trained to accomplish one or a few operations most skillfully rather than ancient craftsmanship which knew how to perform many tasks accurately but not economically. It also requires the introduction of special, single-purpose equipment which will do several tasks at once with a minimum expenditure of time. The full development of special machinery was not reached until forty or more years after Cyrus Hall McCormick's death — nor is it complete even to-day, for men are still pondering and planning to improve the things they do. Nevertheless, it is certain that our wider experience is based upon the pioneering of the past.

It is also interesting in the extreme to discover how far in advance of his time McCormick was in the matter of welfare work. It is recognized in modern industry that an executive should consider the interests of his employees; but it is safe to say that fifty years ago few employers were conscious of the fact that workmen have feelings. Most managers regarded them then merely as another type of machinery whose coöperation could be purchased for so many cents the hour. Not so with McCormick. Possibly because his own early years had been filled with hours of severe toil, he appreciated better than other captains of industry the social and economic importance of the inter-relation of satisfaction and labor. Just before his death he inaugurated a policy of assistance to employees, the most important element of which was the construction of model cottages sold at cost to his men; and he gave land for a church in the vicinity of his factory.

To portray Cyrus Hall McCormick merely as a successful inventor and business man is to miss many of the most significant elements of his character. The great men of all ages have been many-sided; and he certainly possessed that type of mind which is never satisfied by the conquest of one world. As he became wealthy, it was no more than fitting that his thoughts should turn toward donations to his church. As a boy he had been brought up in a highly religious atmosphere. Always serious-minded and not given to the lighter activities of other youths, it was natural for him to exhibit an ever-deepening interest in church affairs. In 1846, when he was urging his brother Leander to go to Cincinnati, one of the advantages of that city in his eyes was its many churches. Chicago, too, appealed to him in 1847 partly because of the strength of the local Presbyterianism. So when he had money to donate to causes, it was second nature for him to seek to further the interests of the Presbyterian Church.

At the 1859 General Assembly, he offered to endow the professorships of the Presbyterian Theological Seminary of the Northwest, provided the institution were removed to Chicago. The account of his frequent gifts to religious education, his energy and enthusiasm for the work of the Seminary which he thus took under his wing, and his overwhelming concern for its affairs, has no proper place in these pages. Nevertheless, his methods were typical of the spirit that went into the development of his business. Just as he was ever eager to cross swords with all and sundry who denied the supreme merit of his reaper and to fill the columns of the newspapers here and abroad with long articles on the invention, so he approached theological debate. His letters were just as full of technical discussion as were his panegyrics on the subject of mechanized agriculture. Woe to the Seminary professor, whether in Chicago or elsewhere, who sought to convince him on some Scriptural or doctrinal point. McCormick sprang to the defense of his own beliefs as hardily as if the controversy concerned the originality of his invention. The Bible, the teachings of Presbyterian leaders, the sermons of those divines who belonged to his school of thought, were one and all marshaled in defense of his points. His correspondence bristles with argument, his logic is pointed with the merciless barbs of supreme self-confidence, his assurance is founded on deep-seated consecration to the cause of Christianity.

In 1873, when religious issues were embittered by the feud between the northern and the southern branches of the Presbyterian Church, he bought a religious newspaper, *The Interior*, and tried through its editorial policy to promote union between the Old and New schools of embattled Presbyterianism. For years he poured money into this publication. He never lost faith in the efficacy of his message. He never saw himself, whether as an inventor or as a private citizen, other than as a missionary ordained to do some service for the world. His pastor said of him, 'He thought of souls as well as machines.' His own creed was simple: 'Business is not inconsistent with Christianity, but the latter ought to be a help to the former, giving confidence and resignation after using all *proper* means.'

Such of his enormous correspondence as I have read gives a fascinating perspective of the scope of McCormick's mind. His public letters, as for example on the Seminary, are forcible, logical, conclusive, and highly combative. His mental processes are indicative not only of a great breadth of vision, but of an assuredness that is superb. One cannot read his massing of evidence upon some obscure point of religious controversy, or upon the reaper, without realizing that he was as much himself convinced by his own argument as he was convincing. His private letters are hurried, compact, and very much abbreviated. His style was a kind of shorthand that tells much of the productively crowded state of his mind. Being a great man, he was not too big for as close attention to details as to the broader aspects of affairs. He shows himself to have been as constructively interested in such matters as the health of his manufacturing staff or the state of national unity. His many letters to his well-loved brother William indicate how close he was to the details of his business. They are filled with discussions of those little points which executives theoretically overlook. But not he: for the reaper was his life.

McCormick never held public office, but he was ever keenly interested in the practice of government. As a Southerner, it was natural that his affiliations should lie with the Democratic Party. An intimate friend of Horace Greeley, he was largely instrumental in aiding that great journalist to argue the case for pacific settlement of the dispute between the North and the South. When the combat which he abhorred could not longer be avoided, he deemed it his privilege to try to bring the warring halves of the Nation together again and spent much time preparing a basis for settlement. He thought of the Nation as an economic unit that should not be divided.

Similarly, by investment and moral support he helped in the completion of the first transcontinental railway system, the Union Pacific; and he was one of the first of

CYRUS HALL McCORMICK (FOURTH FROM LEFT) SHOWN WITH A GROUP OF DISTINGUISHED AMERICAN INVENTORS

From a steel engraving after a painting by Schussele

those men who stood out for the construction of an Isthmian Canal. The development of the Pacific Coast States was a matter at that time beyond any selfish commercial consideration. Nevertheless, the conception of a strong, united, far-flung nation appealed mightily to his imagination. It may have been as well that his experiments in politics never carried him beyond the ownership of two Chicago newspapers, the *Times* and the *Expositor*; and it is not improbable that his powerful influence was more effective as a layman than if, as his friends wished, he had become Senator. After all, his crowded life may have seemed full enough as it was.

There have been few busier men than Cyrus Hall McCormick. No great pioneer has ever been satisfied with an inconclusive life, nor can the possible limits of an active mind be measured in usual terms. A pioneer seeks the remote fastnesses of the unknown because his brain compels him. McCormick invented the reaper and straightway leaped from a Virginia farm to national prominence. He devised ways to manufacture his machine. He pioneered American business toward modern advertising, a bold warranty of product, and a broad system of credit to the customer. He organized quality, canvassing, and service. He envisioned the infancy of foreign trade and labored for its development. He found time for interest in religious, political, and public affairs. In addition to all these matters, he was able to give real attention to the details of the private lives of an immense number of friends, business associates, and dependents. It will never be known how many people sought him out with petty problems, how many troubled men found reassurance in his readily offered store of experience and wisdom. In his last years, when ill health confined him to his house, he was wont to hold a court of counsel in the afternoon. His parlor would be full of people seeking interviews. One after another would be ushered in to him as he sat in his wheel chair, bringing their problems to the judgment seat of his wisdom. No one was ever turned away — the great mind was big enough for all and his sympathy never waned. But once when his infant son was carried in he forgot all else. 'Take him away,' he said to his wife, 'if you want me to have attention for these other matters.'

His marriage in 1857 was one of the happier moments in a life that must seem too much drawn upon by crowding events. During all his younger days he eschewed the society of women. Tall, handsome, dark-haired, impressive in face and figure, a lion of a man in any company, he might have chosen from among the circles of the great. But he had dedicated his career to the business of the reaper and perhaps he felt that the pleasures of feminine companionship were not for him. Yet, when he was forty-eight, he met young Nancy Fowler who was visiting friends in Chicago, was captivated, and married her. Of my revered grandmother I shall have more to relate in another place. Suffice it now to say that, however much Cyrus Hall McCormick may have dedicated his being to great deeds of service, he found in this girl the equal of himself.

Never has there been a man whose days were more consecrated to the work he had made his own. It was his custom to awake at five, consider his problems in the solitude of early morning, and spend the usual waking hours in consultation with his associates and subordinates. After supper he would sleep for two hours in his chair and then, until midnight, he would again engage in interviews and discussions. In these conferences he sometimes seemed deliberate in making up his mind, but once he reached a decision, his purpose was adamant. He practically never went out: the world came to him with its problems and its hopes. He never enjoyed any relaxation except music, never sought the diversion of the theater or society. His purpose in life was so single that he would not hunt a way to those idle mental pastures which men seek for recreation or for growth. He found his rest in activity.

We in this generation have time for those problems only which can be classified by secretaries and organized into systems. He never had a secretary. His wife copied his voluminous letters; his eldest son represented him when he could not be in two places at once. His filing cabinet was his brain or the drawer of his desk. With none of the conveniences which we employ to facilitate our labor, he invented and conducted a business and still maintained mental energy enough to keep an intimate contact with a dozen other matters. Each of these demanded a volume of correspondence that would terrify any one not equipped with typewriters and the like. Each of them received his full attention and his interest. Each of them was vital to his mentality. The secret of his grasp of affairs unquestionably lay in his breadth and force of mind — he could grasp so much more than average men that his thought was not exhausted, but flourished, rather, under the stimulus of activity.

Perhaps Cyrus Hall McCormick was one of those rare men who, in the eyes of weaker mortals, are afflicted with a disease of superactivity. Napoleon was such a man, one of whom other men stood — and still stand — in awe. He could do without sleep, make plans with an unerring aim at success, attend to a score of petty details without losing the perspective of his broad objective, rule destiny as it were — and still remain unfatigued and competent.

No subject was too small for inclusion within the sweep of Oliver Cromwell's intellect. Lincoln possessed understanding as well as courage and a supreme vision of purpose that showed him conclusions far beyond the reach of an average mind. Theodore Roosevelt, as much as any man, combined the vigor of innumerable activities with the force of swift and sure decision; and both with an almost unhuman ability to stretch his intelligence and appreciation to unbelievable limits. So, also, the pioneers who adventured across the Atlantic to discover America, or toiled over the plains to find the limits of the West, were urged onward by the force of their own unleashed energy. One and all, they could carry more in their great minds than normal men. The scope of their activity was not limited by their bodily strength nor did they possess a finite power of absorption. They were successfully, supremely, finely superactive. And so, too, was McCormick.

The number of lawsuits in which he engaged is an interesting commentary on the tenacious vigor of the man. Their total would appall a pacifist. He crossed legal swords with the United States Patent Office, with Hussey, with Seymour and Morgan, with Manny, and with numberless other men. Almost always he lost, but ever he sued — or was sued — because of an inherent faith in the justice of his cause. Call him stubborn if you will, or determined or militant: once he had embarked upon a course planned 'after using all *proper* means,' he could not be swerved from his objective. He did not fight for the mere joy of victory, but for the more desirable aim of justice. His sense of justice was so strong that it gave intensity to his purpose, strength to his will, and nerved him through the long trials of unending perseverance. He had awe and reverence for those things which are true and right. His thorough conviction that justice must prevail made him insensible to reproach and impatient of delay. Justice, of course, was required to measure up to his own reading of the evidence — but it is in such strength of character that the foundations of success are formed.

One of the most character-revealing lawsuits in which he engaged was concerned with what he deemed an over-charge for certain excess baggage on a trip. Enraged, he refused to pay, left the train, and the trunks went on to Chicago without him, to be burned by fire next day. He sued the railway for their value, and then, because his cause immediately became a matter of principle, fought it for over twenty years. In the end, just before his death, he won; and he had spent five times the amount of the damages his estate received. Judged by its result, this litigation may seem purposeless. Perhaps — but even so it is something to believe so bravely in the justice of your position and in its attainment.

A man who thus fights his way through life, beating down opposition with an intolerant disregard, must neces-sarily make personal enemies. It is safe to say that his business competitors hated him, partly because of jeal-ousy for his success and partly because of his ruthless championing of the cause of his reaper. The same quali-ties are at the root of his failure as a politician. But hard as he might be toward an enemy, he always fought his battles in the open: he never in his life spoke disparag-ingly of a man behind his back.

Consider the environment from which McCormick sprang: a Virginia farm. But rural life and rural com-munities have ever furnished the vitality of the Nation. Streets and country highways were then unpaved lanes. Houses were simple, with tall doors and narrow windows, unaffected as yet by the architectural outreachings of a more sophisticated age. Pulpit and post office came to the people jogging a-horseback with the circuit-rider or the contract mail carrier. The village store contained only the barest necessaries of life and not one of the varied luxuries of to-day's drug store or corner grocery. There was no railway station in such a community, no garage, no moving-picture palace — but always a church, always a school, always a blacksmith shop. Of food, there was more than sufficient if crops were good, but it was home-grown, guiltless of the cannery or the packing house; and the simple clothing, perhaps even the Sunday best, was homespun and homesewn. There was no leisure class, for to work for one's livelihood was as natural as to breathe.

Change the picture: it is now Chicago of 1884. We vision the growing, eager, young city instead of the farm and the village. The quiet brick house has become a brownstone mansion decorated with carved paneling and the art of Europe. Presbyterianism and Democracy hurry here for counsel, and the tall reception rooms are thronged with seekers come to ask for aid and gain relief. Cyrus Hall McCormick wears the button of the Legion of Honor, and he has grown rich, but he is still working. The blacksmith shop where his strong young arm beat out a chariot for his fame has become a mighty factory energized by his intellect. The farmer boy has become chief citizen among Chicago's thousands.

His reaper has served him well; so he goes on serving — serving the need of the farmer for relief from labor, answering the cry of the world for bread. His work is done; he must lay down his own share of service. The pioneer must give over his fight. But his work will live.

'Life,' McCormick told his wife as he lay dying in

1884, '*is* a battle.' He had not found it easy. He gained
from it wealth and fame and leadership among men; but
he put into the struggle as much as he took out of it.
Most of all, it seems to me, his success is indicative of the
triumph imagination may gain over the obstacles of sloth
and blind prejudice and the legion of those things which
are held to be impossible simply because no one has yet
accomplished them. Abstract qualities are, after all, the
ultimate test. McCormick did not invent the reaper
simply because he was a natural mechanic, nor devise his
novel business methods purely because he had something
to sell. He had a constructive genius spurred on by the
overwhelming reach of his imagination. He could, by its
aid, have been equally successful in any other age or
place.

There is invariably something fine and challenging in
being the first in a field. We whose lives are so settled by
the limitations of environment, cannot but respect a
pioneering spirit. We envy its ability to project itself
into the unknown and to gain tangible satisfaction out
of the reach of imagination. Throughout all history such
imagination as McCormick's has taught men many
things. It has freed their thought from the shackles of
precedent, led their minds into untrodden paths, helped
them through valleys of indecision and over mountains
of doubt. Imagination cannot be defeated, for it is free;
nor circumscribed, for it is illimitable. It has given the
world the means to satisfy all those wants civilization has
created. Relief from the pains of labor is one of the most
poignant of these; an improved standard of living is
another. As men developed out of the primitive first
into families and then into nations, they found means to
express their desires; and when a certain few became individuals beyond and above the horde of average beings,

our system of life has permitted them to develop. Then comes the crucial test of worth. If the imagination of the rare individual is of permanent value, the effect of his work — the record of his mental stature — will live on after him. It will even increase because of the fine foundation he has provided.

So it was with Cyrus Hall McCormick. His outstanding personality links the reaper with the solution of the problems of our day. He died before the tractor was dreamed of or mass production was named; but his reaper and the business he built were together the progenitors both of a new agriculture and a new concept of industry. However much he accomplished by his own strength, his greatest contribution to the world lies in the fact that the fire of service lit by his imagination burns ever more brightly because of his example.

CHAPTER VI

THE HARVESTER WAR

EARLY on an April morning of 1885, a muttering crowd gathered around the barred gates of McCormick Works. For days the workmen had been on strike. They did not know what their grievances were, but, as happens in labor troubles, an aggressive minority had taught fear to the many who did not want to lay down their tools. There had been inflaming speeches by avowed anarchists, orators who spoke English with mid-European gutturals, about capitalism and the solidarity of the masses. The men were told that their brothers on the street cars and in other factories of Chicago were seething with revolt. The city was in the throes of a newspaper quarrel, a recent panic had left its scars on the financial sinews of the community, and the class hatred which was soon to flare into the tragedy known as the Haymarket Riot was stirring. Seen from the employer's point of view, the city-wide labor disturbances of the hour were a shocking commentary on the instability of political unionism; viewed from the standpoint of the worker, it seemed almost impossible to save enough from low wages to buy bread.

A report traveled through the district that troops might come to protect the factory gates from a rumored attack by the strikers; and they, ready to resist force with force, had collected such arms as they could. They glared up Blue Island Avenue toward the city and waited. A buggy appeared, trotting down the long street; but, expecting to hear the tramp of the militia, they paid it no attention. A young man, bearded and smiling and apparently carefree, drove up. In the face of his confident geniality, and because he was alone, the crowd parted. He waved a good morning, spoke to his horse, and drove through the press to the gate of McCormick Works. Not recognizing him, the crowd gasped at his temerity. He gave an order to the guard within, the gate swung back with a rattle of loosened chains, and he entered. In a moment he reappeared and called to the milling crowd, 'Come on in, boys, if you want to work. The gate is open.'

That man was Cyrus H. McCormick, son of the inventor of the reaper, my father. It is a matter of record that shortly thereafter he raised wages and dismissed the superintendent whose harshness had brewed what real trouble there was.

Cyrus H. McCormick was chosen president of the McCormick Harvesting Machine Company immediately after the death of his father in 1884. As may well be imagined, he, a young man of twenty-five, found it no easy task to step into the place of one of the Nation's leading industrialists. To aid him, he had five years of experience as his father's confidential secretary and representative. He was not unacquainted with the routine of the harvester business, having in his first year at work been entrusted with the monumental task of getting an Appleby-designed McCormick binder into immediate production. He had been in Europe in the interests of the business, had learned to take life seriously because his father would have it so, and had already proved himself to have a calmer, more adaptable point of view than the man who had fought and won the war of the reapers. And yet the son, who was designed by nature for peaceful ways, was to be called to lead his organization through such a fight as the father had never known.

The younger McCormick also had as his best ally the unfaltering support of his mother. Had she lived in other

NETTIE FOWLER McCORMICK
Wife of the inventor
From a photograph made about 1870

times, Nettie F. McCormick would have headed the business herself, or done any one of those things which women now do because they are not merely respected, but are more nearly accorded their deserts. Less than fifty years old in that day, she had been her husband's right hand through half of his business life. Faithful to his every point of view, she had made his interests her own. Renowned for her beauty throughout the courts of Europe, strong in the councils of men, sweet in her understanding of human problems, wise in her farsightedness and knowledge of affairs, she was everything she should have been to be the wife of a pioneer and a leader — herself a great American.

There were few details of the growing business that escaped her. Her correspondence is full of business wisdom beyond the usual interest of women. Consider also one entry in my father's diary, noting an interview he and the general manager of the company had with her at Richfield Springs, New York: 'Butler and I talked with Mother about (1) Pearson Twine Mill question; (2) Indianapolis investment in land for an office building; (3) Proposal to buy a house for B. and his family; (4) Lawsuit against Farwell, etc.; (5) Proposition to buy an interest or whole ownership of coal lands at Des Moines, Iowa.'

American business grew up because its captains, of whom she certainly was one, were not afraid of the details of their affairs. All her life she thus concerned herself with the bricks of the rising structure of the McCormick family business. Even in her last years, I have many times seen her sons go into secret council with her over some matter that troubled them. At the time of her funeral in 1923, many of her personal friends could find no room in the church — it was filled with the Harvester associates whom she loved.

In 1884, there were many pressing issues to solve. There was the matter of the Marquis L. Gorham patents, which anticipated the Appleby twine-binding device in certain respects and had taken on new importance after Gorham's death. McCormick paid Mrs. Gorham $100,000 for them, added them to a pool of patents, and sold manufacturing rights to all competitors. The young president also settled the Gordon case for an infringement upon rights owned by the Gordon brothers and D. M. Osborne. Because it was feared that the check for $225,000 in settlement of the claim might be photographed and used for hostile advertisement, the McCormick attorneys paid the account in small bills. Mr. Osborne stayed late to count the money, carried the satchel containing it to his hotel for the night, lugged it back to Auburn, and there enjoyed what triumph he could by exhibiting it to his men.

During the decade from 1885 to 1895, the implement manufacturers gave much attention to experimental work on freak types of machines. There was the McCormick center-draft mower which, in theory but not in practice, had less side-draft than the standard mower; and a steel binder cut down to weigh less than thirteen hundred pounds, which tested well in its trials, but proved too fragile for actual field use. William N. Whitely rebelled when he was asked to pay royalties under the Gorham patents and worked assiduously on a complicated, delicate machine dubbed 'The Strassburg Clock' by his rivals. Later on, there were numberless attempts to build a 'low-down' grain binder to obviate the necessity of elevating the grain over the main wheel. McCormick actually began production of what was called a 'bindlochine,' and, when it gave evidence of failure, put forth another attempt called a 'tylochine.' Deering gave much attention to one named 'The Prairie Chicken,' but it never got out of the experimental room.

The most noteworthy of the many freak efforts was Mc-Cormick's nearly successful attempt to swing the trade to a right-hand binder. Except for the accident of the reaper tradition, there is no reason why the cutter bar of a grain binder should extend to the left of the main wheel. The platform on all modern tractor-drawn apparatus projects naturally to the right, as does the bar of a mower; but since its inception the standard binder has cut to the left. As competition grew keener, it seemed to be imperative to have new features to talk about, hence the effort to build freak machines. In the middle Nineties, McCormick suddenly and without warning swung its binder production to right-hand harvesters. So great was the pressure of the McCormick sales organization that for a time it appeared as if the effort would succeed; but to save themselves the competitors all leagued against it and invented arguments to answer those invented by the newly converted adherents of right-hand harvesting. McCormick might be the leading company, but it could not quite prevail against the united resistance of all its rivals; and so, in a year or two, it gave over the attempt.

All this experimental effort quite naturally involved an enormous number of field trials. Matters of design had not yet been at all reduced to a science, and many of the new features that were rushed into production and then out to the trade gave the salesmen some momentary vocal advantage. But the 'improvements' were often so hastily prepared that they could not be developed. When a mistake was made, it was incumbent on the territorial experts to correct it in the field. No one could afford to admit failure; or, perhaps, acute salesmanship would conceal a mechanical defect. Every company grasped at any straw — anything that seemed to promise some advantage over competitors. Therefore, the managers of the harvesting machine companies were continually in the field checking the operation of new devices.

The idea of private field tests and public trials was inherent in the McCormick business psychology. All through the sales force there existed the dominant belief that if they could once get their beloved machine in the field, it would easily demonstrate its superiority. Thus, at the time of the World's Columbian Exposition, when the jury wished to make awards without taking the exhibits into grain or grass, the McCormick protest was so vehement that tests were hastily organized. Perhaps one reason for this was that the whole McCormick organization, out of its sixth sense for the niceties of selling, may have been more experimental-minded than its competitors. At all events, there never was a harvest in all the years between 1884 and 1902 when Cyrus H. McCormick's diary fails to record trips to the field to follow new work. Even in 1902, when he went to New York in midsummer to participate in the formation of the International Harvester Company, we find him, three days after the signing of the papers, on an Illinois farm, calmly and as usual attending tests of tedders, rakes, and new types of binder knotters.

McCormick and Deering corn binders were first heard of publicly at the Chicago World's Fair, but none were sold until 1895. The addition of the new implement, a vital factor in so wide a district, was an important event for the field force. Numberless new claims of superiority could be made, numberless new field trials could be staged to prove them. There is an amusing story of the introduction of the rival machines into Iowa which I quote from the report of the McCormick salesman who was there, anxiously awaiting the hour of the public trial:

CYRUS H. McCORMICK
Eldest son of the inventor

We naturally thought we would do the better work, and even to this day I think we did; but that made no difference — the selection of the judges was what counted. The Deering fellows chose a man by the name of McIntosh, who was a gentleman farmer in the summer and an evangelist preacher in the winter. Needless to say, our judge was well primed before the contest. The third man was picked right on the ground the day of the show. They thought they had us, but they placed too much confidence in their man McIntosh. That morning, before we went out to the field, I got hold of him and had a long talk with him about corn binders, explaining the superior merits of the McCormick over the Deering. I was accustomed to selling goods to farmers in those days and was able to convince him that he had made a mistake in lining up with the Deering fellows. He promised me with both hands up that he was well sold and that he would stick. He stuck. When the judges were asked to decide the contest, our man voted for us, the third man voted for Deering, and McIntosh said the McCormick was the best machine. My own opinion is that he was lucky he got away with his life that night.

The opportunity for feats of this kind is not necessarily one-sided. A few years before this corn-binder trial there was a village — which may as well be nameless — peopled largely with German Catholics. They were building a new church, and the Deering traveler was invited by his dealer to donate to the funds, inasmuch as the McCormick traveler had prevailed upon his company to give $20. So the traveler and the dealer wrote to Mr. William Deering about the matter and, because he was a strict Methodist, also dropped the hint that McCormick was selling more machines in the district than all other companies combined. By return mail they received Mr. Deering's check for $250. So when the church was dedicated, the priest exhibited the check and made some very complimentary remarks about 'our very good friend, Mr. William Deering, of Chicago.'

As it so happened, the annual village picnic took place a few days later, and the helpful traveler lavishly bought beer for his friends and (following the usual practice of those days) for potential customers as well. After a time excitement reigned and a song was extemporized, the refrain of which had something to do with 'McCormick $20, Deering $250.' The salesman took orders for twelve binders and thought it legitimate to add an item to his expense account, 'Beer, $10.' But the auditor in Chicago was conversant with Mr. Deering's personal antipathy to alcohol and wrote coldly for an explanation.

The dealer helped the traveler compose a complete narrative of the whole affair from the day the letter was sent asking for a donation to the new church. A somewhat reserved reply advised that under the circumstances the charge could stand, but that no item showing that it was for beer would ever again be allowed. On each annual picnic day thereafter through the years there was an item on the traveler's expense account, 'Sundries, $10.' No explanation was ever asked and Deering continued to outsell McCormick.

These were what might be called practical rather than theoretical methods of distribution. They illustrate the finer side of the old art of salesmanship, for one cannot so effectively change a man's convictions unless one has faith one's self. The framework of the modern sales system had been completed by then and the stream of implement supply was supposed to flow from the company general agency through the dealer to the farmer. But the saturation point of natural absorption had been reached about 1890, and the production capacities of the sixteen larger companies fighting for the business was far in excess of the normal demand. The jobber had already disappeared in the face of the desire of the companies to own their own branches and thus get closer to the ultimate consumer. Such a system of distribution tied up much invested capital in property and stocks of machines and bore heavily on treasuries which were none too robust. The better companies with the most easily salable product required at least one hundred and fifty dollars of capital to do one hundred dollars of annual business, while many of the smaller organizations needed two hundred dollars. They all had to try to find ways of increasing their volume to help carry the load. Hence it was that convincing salesmen of the type of the Deering blockman, or of him who persuaded McIntosh to stick, were in demand.

The rank and file of the McCormick field force were past masters at the art of salesmanship, and it may be that many of the extreme methods practiced upon them (they soon learned to give back as much as they had to take) were a direct reaction from their success. An ex-Deering general agent has told me how hopeless it was for him to go against the pressure of four surrounding Mc-Cormick branches — especially since time was to choose two International Harvester presidents and one vice president from among the four. Frequently, even, this expert sales pressure proved stronger than the company itself had anticipated and the demand for goods was larger than the company could supply. Deering possessed the complementary advantage of a far-seeing manufacturing policy and was willing to take chances by making machines further in advance. It is also possible that Deering more accurately estimated the great future growth the industry was to experience, partly on account of the general revival of business following the McKinley election in 1896, and partly as a result of the sales pressure exerted by all of the companies in general and by Mc-Cormick in particular.

The McCormick ability to sell goods originated largely in an unswerving adherence to the principle of getting out into the territory to look for business. The first agents established throughout the West were usually stationed in county towns where farmers would congregate to attend to their legal and commercial affairs. Before 1890, there were few railways other than transcontinental lines, and it would have been purposeless to establish a network of dealers who could not be reached. Thus the county agent, as he was called, came to feel he had a monopoly on the business in his district; and, furthermore, he was accustomed to having the farmers come in from the country and seek him out. As the network of railways spread across the West, outlying communities began to be developed, agents in smaller towns could be reached, and the harvesting-machine business began to drift into the hands of men who would go out after it. It is perhaps needless to say that as soon as a railway penetrated a new district, one of the first passengers to alight at a hitherto isolated community was a McCormick representative looking for a dealer.

The McCormick Company had in previous years built up the best force of county agents, but by 1890 they had become an outworn institution. Harvesting-machinery distribution could not be fostered by a stay-at-home dealer waiting in his store for business to come to him. More intensive local distribution was demanded. The only type of dealer acceptable to the McCormick traveler was one who would canvass every inch of his territory as aggressively as could be done before the advent of the motor-car. Thus again, as in the early days of the reaper, the ever-efficient triumvirate of pioneer agriculture, aggressive local commerce, and an able industrial policy working from afar, was collaborating to develop farm life on the prairies.

The former methods of advertising, such as catalogues, testimonials, and lists of available prospects, were broadened to suit the new situation. Propaganda which depended on innuendo and inference as much as upon direct statement was introduced. Thus, Deering made much of a supposed history of the reaper, minimizing or omitting the 1831 invention. McCormick's reply was a direct appeal to public opinion. Here, for example, is a picture of one of the first of the 'delivery days' which soon became a regular part of farm implement propaganda:

Every man who bought one of our machines was to take delivery of it on the same day. He was to bring in his family to town and we were to give them all a good dinner and a good big day, and the machines were all to be put in line on the street. We had three hundred McCormick binders in the procession. It was a beautiful day, as fine as the Lord ever made. I hired three bands and put big banners and streamers across the street. I put five or six beautiful floats in the parade and rode myself in a big two-seated carriage. I guess I was a bigger man that day in Carroll than the President of the United States. I gave the town about the biggest day of its history. I engaged all the Ladies' Aid Societies to cook the dinner, hired the theater, gave them a nice little vaudeville turn, and made a speech which the audience was good enough to applaud — I presume because I was paying for it!

Business methods of this kind are perhaps highly picturesque and they are legitimate, judged even by the standards of these more conservative days. Nevertheless, they represent the type of salesmanship which put all competitors and all dealers too much on their mettle to get business. Therefore, before the harvester war ended with the formation of the International Harvester Company, competition changed from hard rivalry to unending strife. Salesmanship became a brave but vicious battle in which it was deemed that loyalty to one's company demanded that organized hate be the order of the day. Friendships were broken; rivals refused to drink a glass at the same bar; any means that would down a competitor was considered legitimate; prices were slaughtered indiscriminately and without regard to profits; funds were squandered on senseless attempts to prove superiority; and business was habitually conducted in a way that brought the industry to the verge of bankruptcy. The final result of the harvester war was to be consolidation or destruction.

It is not necessary to infer that, officially, there ever was such a period as that which I have called the harvester war, any more than there ever was an officially admitted feud between McCormick and Hussey or McCormick and Manny. But the inventor's correspondence bristles with enough hostility toward these two men, and indeed toward all those competitors who he believed had transgressed upon his private preserve, to have permitted commentators to characterize the business quarrels of the early days as the war of the reapers. Similarly, however suave the official record may seem, the recollections of the men who were engaged in the harvesting-machine business in the Nineties bristle with enough charge and counter-charge, attack and defensive-offensive, cut and thrust, to have characterized a dozen decent military engagements. Like produces like. The harvester men of the middle period were skilled in that kind of training they had received from their warring predecessors. Their descendants of to-day have, with different and more cultivated weapons, fought as bitter, though not as dreadful, a battle. I have no compunction in calling the record of those years a harvester war.

Perhaps, if the device of the field test had never been propounded, there would not have been any harvester

THE FOUR MAJOR HARVESTING MACHINES OVER WHICH THE BATTLES OF THE 'HARVESTER WAR' WERE WAGED: GRAIN-BINDER, MOWER, HAY-RAKE, AND CORN-BINDER

war; but then this story would have been less picturesque. In former times it had been McCormick and Hussey who stormed England and captured columns in the press for their arena. Now it was McCormick *versus* Deering or McCormick *versus* Champion or Milwaukee or Wood or some one else. Always, it was McCormick, the great exponent of salesmanship, on one side, and some one else on the other striving to take away the leadership which McCormick possessed. The war was certainly severe; but the men of to-day's 'old guard' are willing to remember those years as 'the good old days.' Much benefit — including Harvester Spirit and present-day service to farmers — came out of them, so perhaps they need not be regretted.

Take Whitely, for example, who for a time after the death of Cyrus Hall McCormick performed such prodigious acts that he was called 'The Reaper King.' His chief feat, which won him his first fame, was to hitch himself in the place of a horse and himself pull one of his mowers to prove its light draft. Perhaps he had heard of the deeds of one of the brothers Marsh, who once, unaided, bound an acre of grain in fifty-five minutes to demonstrate the simplicity of the early harvester. It was men of this type, men like the first Crusaders, who not only led their followers into war, but themselves swung the heaviest battle-axe, who made field tests spectacular. They even devised the ultimate test of 'merit' in which two reapers, chained together back to back, were pulled apart to prove their strength.

Concerning the field tests of the Nineties, when the rest of the harvesting-machine world was trying to wrest from McCormick the supremacy it had won, a former factory repair man writes: 'No friendly rivalry out on the firing line — lots of dirty tricks pulled off, tinkering with rival machines at night. Many a pitched battle I have heard the field men tell about. Who won the field trials? Why, Deering, I suppose; at least, I never heard of any one else winning!' They were loyal to their cause, those men of old!

There is the story of Champion's great effort with a new mower, produced in 1899, when it challenged all comers and laid down the rule that the machines striving for the prize were to be operated by a competitor's employee, driven against a solid post, and were then to cut grass. McCormick 'took up the challenge and we were the only competitor who did. Our first go was at Clare, a little town in Webster County, Iowa. We had an expert named Dan who was a fearless fellow. When he drove their mower against the post, the cutter bar bent right back between the wheels. He drove the team with such speed against the post that it broke the shoe and they nearly went mad. Their driver broke the pole off our machine, and there were the two machines practically a wreck.'

Such tests may seem ridiculous in the light of to-day's practices which seek to keep machinery in order and to prove its worth by operation; but to-day's are not the means of 'the good old days' when competing salesmen sought to sell machines by direct methods. There is the tale of a farmer who, to his sorrow, let it be known in a group of machine men that he was a prospect for a grain binder. So persistent were they in their clamoring for attention that the poor man was soon constrained to seek refuge in a hotel room. When the slight protection of a locked door availed him nothing against the swarm of canvassers, he jumped out of the window.

In truth, the field men of the competing companies could not be restrained by such a thing as company regulations when they were out after business. Policies were swayed by an army of fighters to whom results were the only test. Competition grew so severe and unbusiness-like that the members of the leading organizations became enemies, not in a personal sense, but, like soldiers, believing that the thing had to be done. Anything the old-time men could do to the other fellow to knock him out was considered legitimate. At one time the various company presidents issued a joint order, over their own, well-recognizable signatures, to cease the breaking-up of competitors' sales — but the fight went on.

It became customary for a farmer who had bought one make of binder to receive a call from the salesman of another company, who would then seek to convince him of the futility of ever expecting to gather his harvest with the make of implement he had just acquired. If the salesman was a good talker — and most of them were — the farmer would be persuaded to haul the first implement back to town on some charge of poor operation and buy the rival. There is a bizarre tale of a farmer who bought one type, but woke up next morning to find quite another make standing in his yard and his own purchase nowhere to be seen. In a certain district, even, a 'wrecking crew' was maintained to tamper with rival machines and create dissatisfaction with their performance.

To illustrate the combination of true commercial fighting worth and the uneconomic ridiculousness of unbridled competition, I repeat a rather long story of what happened after a certain McCormick binder had been sold not far from Pomeroy, Iowa. The story comes from the general agent who fought that day for the honor of his cause:

Our dealer telegraphed me that Champion had pulled into the same field where he had sold an eight-foot McCormick

binder and that the situation was desperate, as they were trying to break up our sale. When I got there, the farmer was in
trouble with our machine, and the Champion boys had put
plenty of poison in him about me. He was swearing loudly and
wouldn't speak to me, so I waited. When I got a chance I
talked to him mildly, which seemed to surprise him after the
reputation as a bluffer those fellows had given me. I showed
him where his four-horse eveners were not put on right, with
the result that two horses were pulling the whole load. Finally
I got the eveners fixed and loosened up the compressor so the
machine worked satisfactorily. But Champion had made him
some kind of a special price; also, they had notified every purchaser of a McCormick binder in the neighborhood to come
and see this binder fail, with a view of getting them to cancel
their McCormick orders.

I pointed out to the farmer that the Champion was a six-foot
cut against our eight, and showed him that even so the Champion was not taking a full cut. The crop was barley, and it had
crinkled down and lay like a crow's nest. The soil was an old
peat bog that had burned, and now it was a very slippery job. I
had my work cut out for me to make the eight-foot binder operate without choking. So that night I got up at three o'clock,
drove out to the farm and woke the farmer up. He was dressed
only in his old hickory shirt that he had been wearing the previous day, because pajamas and nightgowns were not yet fash-
ionable in his neighborhood. He put on his pants and came out
to the barn and we had a long talk. I gave him such a sales talk
he was absolutely convinced the McCormick machine was the
one he wanted. No difference what the Champion would be
able to do next day, it was settled.

Well, a big crowd of machine men had come to the hotel that
night and the Deering fellows said they would come in too and
show us both up. There were at least one hundred and fifty
farmers there, and the Deering was the first to start. They had
a brand-new machine and four big gray horses, and the horses
and the machine were decorated with little flags. But when the
first bundle of tangled barley came through the binder, it
choked and the bull wheel buried itself in the slippery soil and
they were done. The farmer was driving our binder himself and
was having no trouble, although I am not prepared to say

whether he cut a full eight feet all the way around or not. But
the Champion dealer got a handful of straw and tried to put
it secretly on our elevator chains, to prove his claim that our
chains would pull grain out of our open elevator and wind it
around the sprockets. I grabbed him by the neck and he fell
down in the stubble. Then the Champion fellows started for
me, but somebody got between us. They started to abuse the
farmer, who was a big, powerful man, and he struck the Champion dealer. His old father stopped the fight. But the contest
broke up in a row, and they left in disgrace without having
driven us from the field.

That general agent has, with the passing of time, gained
a different perspective on the feats of his younger, more
embattled years. He ends thus his account of what must
have been an ofttimes repeated skirmish:

This story is related simply to give an idea of the expense of
doing business in those days and to what silly lengths excessive
competition led us in those ridiculous fights. I suppose we were
just a product of those times.

There can be no question that under such a system the
cost of making a sale was high. Sometimes two rival
general agents would rouse themselves to battle and, regardless of instructions from the home office, would slash
prices in a progressive and widening effort to get the
upper hand of a competitor. In Grand Rapids in 1899, for
example, grain binders were sold for half the standard
wholesale price. It should be remarked that the Mc-
Cormick men now say they then invariably acted on the
defensive. But if I know them at all, their defense of their
traditional leadership was vigorous, to say the least.

Another tale suggests how unfavorably this inordinate
pressure to sell machines must have affected credits. A
harvesting-machine man was driving through an isolated
part of Nebraska and saw a new Milwaukee binder in a

friend's yard. Knowing this farmer had no grain at all to cut, the traveler stopped to inquire. The farmer had wanted a hammer and a wrench and had no money to buy them nor any credit; so he bought the binder, all on time, to get the tool box!

It must not be thought that business excesses of this kind were perpetrated by a horde of city-bred, factory-trained men who did not know farming conditions. The members of the harvesting-machine field armies were recruited in the country and themselves supplied the material from which the executive staffs of another business generation were drawn. Many a lowly 'expert,' announcing himself proudly to the farmers as a factory man, was a farmer boy who had shown himself capable of remedying his own mechanical troubles. Machinery was a mysterious thing to farmers, and an owner's diagnosis of trouble was usually wrong. Hence the invariably neces-sary practice of 'fixing the farmer first.' Nevertheless, the mechanical success of the experts was, on the whole, remarkable. They fought the harvester war as bitterly and as blithely as did the salesmen and they believed as profoundly in the innate justice of their particular cause. Witness, for example, the expert known across Ontario for his skill who, untactfully but loyally, interrupted a farmer's complaint with 'Aw — you don't know what th' hell you're talking about. This machine was made by the best company in the world and was made to work and it *will* work. Let me get at it!'

The methods of the harvester war were unquestion-ably undesirable. They can be excused only because the generation which developed them to the wildest extent had inherited the spirit of warfare from revered forbears. They were not countenanced by the heads of the Mc-Cormick or Deering or other companies, but they were, nevertheless, a tribute to the loyalty which those leaders inspired in their men. It was not merely ambition which led those 'old boys' through sacrifice to beat one another to a sale, or into subterfuge to defeat a competitor. The men of the old companies never cared to meet a rival socially, and they would willingly neglect their private lives to advance the interests of their house. Many of them have gone ahead and some are still active in positions of high responsibility. But it was not chance for promotion that inspired them to endure the rigors of the furious days of bitter competition — it was loyalty. Loyalty builds character — and it is also possible that out of the strife of 'the good old days' there has come, by reaction from the practices of the past, much that is most desirable in the methods of the present.

The leaders who were directing the marshaling of the harvesting-machine armies between 1884 and 1902 knew very well that such competition as they saw going on around them could not but prove disastrous to their business. The idea of amalgamation was first broached between Cyrus Hall McCormick and William Deering before the former's death, but nothing came of purely tentative conversations. The temper of the first generation of harvester men was too individualistic. The records of 1885 are full of accounts of meetings called to consider consolidation and adjourned with nothing done. McCormick stood on one side for individual activities, Deering did not then participate in the discussions, and the smaller companies were urging consolidation or, at least, some understanding on prices. In 1888, there were other meetings from which McCormick kept away. Late in 1890, the first consolidation, the American Harvester Company, was born.

At that time all the harvester companies bought their

knives and cutting sections from the Whitman, Barnes Company, of Akron, Ohio. Its president, Colonel A. L. Conger, conceived the idea of a grand consolidation of all existing producers of harvesting machinery in which his own little organization would be preserved. So, as he went around to call on his customers, he propounded his plan and finally persuaded each of them to set a price on his property. Thus, in December, 1890, the many competitors found themselves all members, for the moment, of the same family. Cyrus H. McCormick was president, William Deering was chairman of the board of directors, E. K. Butler, general manager of the McCormick Company, held a similar position in the new organization, and minor offices were apportioned among the other companies.

The scrambled executives met in the Champion building in Chicago. It soon became a matter of interesting inquiry how the new company was to find money to pay the fantastic valuations on the old properties accepted without appraisal by Conger. There was also immediate and widespread public opposition to this 'trust' as being an effort to flout the recently passed Sherman Law. It was also whispered about in the office that the widow of the late inventor of the reaper would not willingly see his name submerged in the new company. Finally, there was no operating plan nor, most disastrous of all, was there any operating capital.

The American Harvester Company died in January, 1891, when Cyrus H. McCormick and William Deering went to New York for advice. They found that the bankers whom they consulted were cold to the new company and were unwilling to provide the necessary financing. The two Chicago men were sharing a hotel parlor, where, late at night, McCormick was pondering the situation. As

SOME OF THE WARRIORS WHO MADE FARM-MACHINE HISTORY DURING THE PIONEER YEARS OF THE INDUSTRY

Left to right, above: Hussey, Manny, McCormick, Deering, Appleby
Below: Osborne, Bushnell, Marsh, Miller, Wood

he sat alone, the door of Deering's room opened. Clad only in his nightshirt, the old gentleman walked in and stood before the fireplace, his hands locked behind his back, and his fine face grave with concern.

'McCormick,' he said at last, 'are these other fellows trying to make the two of us carry water for them?'

'It looks that way to me!'

'All right, let's go home and call it off.'

'I agree,' said the younger man — and both went to bed and slept soundly for the first time in nights, secure again in the unimpaired possession of their own sound companies.

The next endeavor to effect a consolidation in the harvesting-machine industry did not take place for several years. In the meantime competitive strife waxed, and certain of the smaller companies, which had completed the abortive roster of the American Harvester Company, had gone the way of all weak contestants in a struggle which tested the souls of the strongest. McCormick and Deering were all the time standing out more clearly as the leading antagonists; and in 1897 they very nearly solved by themselves the problem of their rivalry. It was then proposed that the McCormicks should buy out the Deerings, who were willing to retire. A purchase price for the entire business was agreed on, an option was taken, and Cyrus H. McCormick and his brother Harold started out to try to find the money. Perhaps they were financially inexperienced, or perhaps their figures did not sufficiently set forth the probable benefits of consolidation. At all events, they were unable to get the necessary money together before their option on the Deering business expired.

An opportunity which must then have seemed priceless thus vanished and the harvester war went on. It was dur-

ing the period immediately following 1897 that the greatest Deering effort to overhaul McCormick was made.
Deering anticipated McCormick in making hay rakes,
binder twine, knives and other cutting apparatus, and
malleable castings, and in the construction of a rolling
mill. It was planning a Canadian factory, a blast furnace, and the acquisition of ore and timber reserves. A
successful radical anticipation of sales requirements had
been allowing it to fill orders after McCormick had sold
out its stocks of machines. All in all, the Deerings were
closing the gap that separated them from the leader in
the race

It was mutually apparent that on the competitive basis
then existing, Deering could not afford to go on expanding
nor could McCormick secure enough capital to build or
buy a steel mill of its own and provide production facilities to repel the Deering drive. Expansion in the foreign
field, where McCormick stood first, was expensive; and
Deering could not afford to try to catch up, nor could Mc-
Cormick further extend itself. Business was still reasonably profitable for the two leaders, but the added returns
from the much greater volume of the last two or three
years was nowhere near in proportion to the growth.
Even for them the harvester war was disastrous.

CHAPTER VII

FORMATION OF THE INTERNATIONAL HARVESTER COMPANY

IN JUNE, 1902, the president of the McCormick Harvesting Machine Company went to New York to seek the aid of the House of Morgan. He had for some time been viewing with apprehension the growing competitive strength of Deering. It would matter comparatively little to the trade if the weaker companies failed to live through the bitter war of the last decade. If Wood or Johnson or Acme went down, that would not lighten the burden of those who bore the responsibilities of leadership. Deering was the rival McCormick had to fear — McCormick was the leader whose place Deering was trying to occupy.

In the case of both these companies there was more to fight for than the victory of the moment. One of them had a history to defend, the long tradition of a leadership that had lasted for sixty years. There was a reputation to preserve that had been won in the bitter battles of industrial evolution. The family business was a memorial to its founder. It was in the hands of men who were living out of and by Cyrus Hall McCormick's ideals. It was supervised by the kindly figure of his widow whom the new generation adored, whether they were young gladiators or whether they were the scarred survivors of the army he himself had trained. One and all loved her because they saw in her the living manifestation of him who had planned their destinies. In the case of the Deering Company there was an honorable record of commercial success to uphold and the triumphant memory of twenty years of increasing challenge to the old leader. Those two decades of harvester experience had taught it the rules of the rough-and-tumble of competition, had bestowed upon it the atmosphere of respect which weaker men hold for the brains of giants, had proved that adroitness and clever planning and skill were nearly a match for tradition and the intangible power which always goes with leadership.

Three times McCormick and Deering had met around a table, three times their peace conferences had failed, three times they had gone out to renewed battle. Recently Deering had been exhibiting new tactics. Since the frontal attack gave no promise of final success, new strategy was being tried. The field of raw materials was being explored. Deering built a rolling mill near his plant where old railway rails and other steel could be reworked into the special shapes and sizes demanded for harvester manufacture. He had acquired a controlling interest in a South Chicago blast furnace, iron ore deposits on the Mesaba Range, and Kentucky coal lands, which gave evidence of his intention to produce his own iron and steel. He bought hardwood forests in Missouri and yellow pine in Mississippi. If he could himself provide his own iron, steel, and lumber, the basic raw materials of the agricultural implement industry, he might be able to reduce the material cost of his machines. He had long since shown himself to be a most worthy manufacturing foeman and by this time his factory was more self-contained than McCormick's.

The McCormick Company's greater genius lay in the sales field. Its selling system, pioneered by the founder of the business a half-century before, kept it supreme. But now McCormick wanted to do as Deering had done, to acquire raw material resources and develop its factories; and it desired to expand further in foreign countries where Deering was not as strongly represented. But capital was lacking. So, to get money for the sinews of the battles of the future, Cyrus H. McCormick went to New York.

Quietly, unannounced, armed simply with a letter of introduction, trained in the hardest warfare of commerce but unskilled in the high science of finance, he approached George W. Perkins, youngest of the partners of J. P. Morgan and Company. He explained his errand, and Perkins assured him that the necessary capital could easily be secured. Then the financier began to ask questions about the harvester business, its backgrounds, the companies engaged in it, their strength, the ability of their leaders, the value of their properties and products, the chances for further development at home and abroad. For hours the two men talked. Before McCormick left, Perkins inquired if by any chance he cared to merge his business in a larger company in which the McCormick business would be the dominating element.

A week later they met again, and Perkins was given the voluminous data prepared for the most recent effort at consolidation. At the same time he announced that the Morgan firm might find it interesting itself to enter the harvester business, and asked how he might go about it to buy the assets of the Milwaukee Harvester Company, whose ruling dynasty had become extinct. That day, when McCormick left, Perkins invited him to return in July for an extended series of conferences. A third time McCormick went back to New York. For three weeks, through the blistering heat of a Manhattan summer, he and his attorneys lived in their hotel and received frequent calls from Perkins. The banker went rapidly from one to another of the groups of harvesting-machine men whom he had invited to New York, pointing out the advantages of consolidation and settling the basic principles. My father has said that Perkins was the most brilliant negotiator he ever met. He and the other Chicagoans knew little of the fine details of finance, nothing intimately of Perkins — and yet in three weeks the banker won the confidence of all of them, merged their businesses, and accomplished the one thing they knew would be their salvation, though they had tried in vain for eleven years to effect it — consolidation.

The harvester men met together for the first time around a Morgan conference table in late July. Perkins talked again of the benefits to them and to their customers of a consolidated industry, of economies in manufacturing and in distribution, of foreign fields waiting to be developed. He talked of his proposed financial structure and the new conquests of new fields of endeavor that would result. He talked so well and painted such a rosy picture of the future that his listeners almost forgot their ancient differences and were willing to try to be friends.

There can be no question but that self-preservation lay uppermost in the minds of the company presidents who sat around that table. The evils of the harvester war were fresh in their troubled minds. But there were many other cogent reasons why the International Harvester Company should be formed. The competitive methods of the Nineties were not only murderous, but wasteful in the extreme and detrimental to retail agent and consumer as well as to manufacturer. Farmers had bought enormous quantities of harvesting machinery in 1902 from the five organizations, more than they really needed. The pressure of salesmanship was such that the harvester companies were forcing more implements on the public than it had any occasion to buy. A machine which might have lasted for nearly ten years was declared obsolete in less than five; and the farmer's bill for new equipment was beyond all reason — not because of the price per unit, which was ruinously low, but because of the many units needlessly sold. The local dealers were crippled by their own numbers. Competition had decreed that all over the United States, in every town, at every crossroads, there must be a McCormick or a Deering dealer. The three other companies were less widely represented; but they, too, had flung as far as possible the array of their distributors. More than forty thousand dealers across the land were too many. None of them could grow, none could become prosperous, none could do more than imitate in his own neighborhood the feud methods of the big companies. They fought, too, and their fall was even more rapid.

The big companies did not realize clearly that they were producing and selling more machines than the trade could absorb. They felt that if normal conditions could be imposed upon them, they would be able not only to make their business profitable, but might expand it as well. They were certain that this could be done in the foreign field if only they could get the necessary capital for expansion. McCormick, and to a lesser extent Deering, were both already established abroad, and each was in its own way striving to pour out its strength to win in Europe and Siberia the victories each was fighting for at home. But compared to America, foreign farms were underequipped. Branch houses and local agents were needed, also stocks of machines and repairs. Trained men were required to carry the gospel of mechanized farming to struggling peasants. Those were things which capital and husbanded strength alone could supply. J. P. Morgan was then in Europe, in touch by cable with the state of affairs. His keen mind saw the possibilities of developments abroad, and it was he who gave the name 'International' to the new company.

The harvester men expected also to accomplish large manufacturing and distributing economies out of the consolidation which would benefit both stockholders and customers. But after the new company was under way, they found to their sorrow that the undue sales pressure of the days of cut-throat competition had pushed the volume beyond all reason. They had to face such a serious reduction of the volume of production that any hope of lower manufacturing or selling costs was vain. In 1903, the International Harvester Company did less business than the constituent companies had done the year before.

An immediate benefit resulting from the amalgamation was the plan, not originally formulated, but soon to be developed, of filling idle factories and curing the abuse of part-time operations with various new lines of product. When a factory made only such strictly seasonal goods as grain binders, twine, mowers, rakes, corn binders, and a few other collateral tools, its schedule of operation was either up or down, depending upon the weather or the fortune of competitive sales efforts. Whole armies of workmen had to be dismissed for many months a year; the capital invested in factory buildings and expensive equipment stood idle too much of the time. It was the same in the field. As soon as harvest was over, the best salesmen were retained to help with collections, but the others were turned loose. By the time winter set in, the collectors also were dismissed, and the battalions waited in unremunerative idleness until spring. Just how this situation might be corrected was not immediately apparent in 1902. There was no expectation that the decline in the volume of harvester business would provide factory space for new lines which would contribute in later years to a steady cycle of manufacturing. However, it was obvious that the evil of part-time operation could not

INTERNATIONAL HARVESTER BINDERS IN ALGERIA AND
IN FRANCE

be cured under the existing circumstances. The future profits of the Harvester Company were to come, not from any expansion of the 'old lines,' but from the business to be built up in later years in other lines of agricultural implements and in lines of trade that were not even dreamed of in the early part of the twentieth century.

A few days after the worried company presidents had heard the last of George W. Perkins' brilliant conversation, on August 12, 1902, they agreed to merge in a new type of corporate structure. To steer clear of the anti-trust clauses of the Sherman Law, Perkins' lawyers planned to buy, not the stock of the constituent companies themselves, but their physical assets only — their factories, their warehouses, their properties, and their inventories. For these the companies received $60,000,000. Another $50,000,000 of the future capital came from their bills and accounts receivable, which, after being guaranteed by their owners, were used as cash in payment for stock in the new company. Ten millions of stock was issued to Morgan for cash. It is interesting to note that, when the stipulated appraisement of properties was made some months later, the assets for which $60,000,000 was paid were found to have an actual value of over $67,000,-000. There was not one dollar of watered stock in all the $120,000,000 capital of the International Harvester Company.

The estates of the owners of the Milwaukee Company received cash for their assets and subscribed to none of the new stock. The Champion representatives took cash for their factories, but paid for their share of stock with their receivables. The Plano people, the Deerings, and the McCormicks asked for and received payment entirely in stock. They had confidence in the future.

The harvester presidents also agreed to tie up the entire capital for ten years in a voting trust composed of Cyrus H. McCormick, the new president, Charles Deering, the new chairman of the board of directors, and George W. Perkins. For ten years this voting trust was to exercise all of the normal powers of stockholders. Its nominal purpose was to carry the company through its first years and to retain control in the hands of the old harvester families. But Perkins had sensed that no McCormick and no Deering could long remain at peace with each other; and out of that sure difference of opinion and objective his brilliant and ever-active mind may have planned some form of control for himself. Be that as it may, the voting trust served to tide the new company over a difficult trial period and to keep it out of the field of speculation during its formative years.

It is not surprising that the formation of the International Harvester Company did not immediately bring peace within the battle-scarred ranks of the harvester legions. While the July and August conferences were continuing in New York, the harvester war was being carried on as strenuously as ever on the territory. None were in the secret of the consolidation except the chiefs. None knew that the lions of to-day were expected to give over their carnivorous habits and be the lambs of to-morrow. When word came that a peace treaty had been signed, each side mourned as if in defeat. These men of the fighting front had been trained too long in the rigor of mortal combat to believe that the feud could be settled in any other way than by the survival of the fittest.

The new organization had been put together in such a brief space of time that there had obviously been opportunity for agreement in principle only. Every detail had to be left for subsequent adjudication. This put a heavy burden on the executive committee of the directors whose duty it was to solve every unsettled problem. Perkins had been the arbitrator during the days leading up to the consolidation; and now, when meetings were held either in New York or Chicago, he tactfully suggested that the interested parties to any intramural dispute endeavor to reach a solution by themselves before taking the case to the court of last resort. But the property appraisals could not be made for months, and even when they were complete, there was much natural but happily unfounded suspicion of the worth of the figures supplied for inventory and other valuations. The new partners still had to learn to trust one another and mutual agreement was not easy.

For a year it was not practical even to put the Company together physically. Probably it would have been impossible to make an instant and yet fair and impersonal choice between the offices, warehouses, personnel, and business methods which now had to be scrambled. Therefore, the component sales organizations were left intact, being simply renamed divisions of the new corporation. The men of the McCormick, Deering, and other battalions were told to cease firing and to coöperate with their former foes; and yet they could see no visible change in their situations. Quite naturally each group sought to consolidate whatever gains it had made and, to be on the safe side, to secure any possible additional advantage against the day of reckoning.

The harvest of 1902 was no more than half over when the consolidation was announced. Many machines still had to be sold, more had to be delivered to purchasers. Field men, who had in the past been trodden upon by more powerful competitors, believed their day had come and assumed an authority they could not otherwise have claimed. General agents, who had formerly had things more or less their own way, resented what they considered the intrusion of unworthy allies. Each division tried so to conduct itself that when the total was rendered, its relative standing would appear as large as possible. Competition, somewhat hidden under the guise of corporate relationship, went on, and, because stepbrothers are prone to be jealous rather than friendly, veiled suspicion became the order of the day.

The more or less separate divisions were maintained until the end of 1903, by which time the executive management was able to get control of the situation. Even in Chicago there had been difficulties, which, while they have now happily been forgotten, caused much heartburning. There was striving for place, there was the natural inability of former rivals immediately to see good instead of bad in one another, and above all there were the scarcely healed scars of the McCormick-Deering duel. Many a former partisan found himself serving under an erstwhile opponent, and many were the sacrifices demanded in the interest of harmony. One eager man went to the president with a complaint about the incompetency of his recently appointed superior. He was urged to remember the need for team-play, to go to bat for his organization and make safe hits.

'But, sir,' said the anguished partisan, 'what I'm talking about isn't a hit — it's a foul!'

As soon as the physical consolidation could be made effective, things began to improve. For ten years the affairs of the International Harvester Company remained in the ultimate control of the three voting trustees; and the final solution of jealousy-bred, petty friction did not come until the flowering of company spirit at the expiration of the voting trust. At the worst, though, the early troubles were caused by misplaced faith in ancient ways or by an overzealous desire to keep the flag of the old house flying. There is something worthy of praise even in misdirected loyalty; and the woes of those brief days may perhaps be charitably regarded as a tribute to the hardiness of the scarred veterans of the harvester war. It is to be regretted that their courage was not rewarded by an increasing volume of business. No one had any idea how large a portion of the volume had been secured by over-persuading the farmer to buy.

The average number of binders annually sold for the five years prior to 1902 was 152,000, whereas for the first ten years of the International Harvester Company it was 91,000. Where an average of 217,000 mowers had been marketed, now no more than 170,000 were required. Even in 1912, the United States business done in the old lines was less than it had been at the time of the creation of the organization that was intended to permit the harvester business to devote its energies to expansion rather than to continued mutual strife!

This decline of the old harvesting-machine lines continued during the first ten International Harvester years in spite of the fact that the acreage of farmed land and the production of grain in the United States were increasing. But the Company's total business prospered at the same time from the successive introduction of more and more 'new-line' machines, such as harrows, cultivators, and cream separators, which one after the other were added to the sales catalogue. Soon after 1902, also, the sale of steel and fiber became an important part of the volume. Most of all, though, the rapidly developing foreign business bolstered Harvester's position.

After 1902, the new capital, new material resources, new blood, and the new enthusiasm for foreign activity promoted by the consolidation brought about a rapid advance in oversea trade. Within four years the foreign business doubled. The trade with Russia alone was approximating the entire export trade of 1902, and South America was buying as much agricultural equipment as all of Europe had formerly ordered. After ten years the Company was widely effective in Great Britain, all over western and Central Europe, Russia, South America, the Antipodes, and Africa. True to the old traditions, it had penetrated into districts where progress was unknown, and, in far countries where peasant farmers had never dreamed of emancipation, it had developed new business by teaching the better methods of mechanized agriculture. American workmen were busy manufacturing articles for the farms of prince and peasant alike. American salesmen were following along the highway of distant commerce pioneered in 1851 by Cyrus Hall McCormick when he visited London with his 'cross between a flying machine, a wheelbarrow, and an Astley chariot.' So well had they taught the people of other countries the use of American harvesting machinery that within ten years the Company's foreign trade had increased fivefold.

The development in the new lines of agricultural equipment was almost as rapid as the growth of the export trade. This began with the purchase in 1903 of D. M. Osborne & Company, of Auburn, New York. Thus, this famous old harvester and tillage business entered International Harvester's ranks and the first step in the direction of a rounded-out line of machinery was taken. The Osborne firm enjoyed a considerable trade in the eastern part of the United States and had already developed a large foreign business; and its twine mill, situated near the seaboard, would, it was hoped, prove a valuable asset in securing foreign twine trade. It was the largest and strongest among the independent concerns, and, since it did a minimum of business in the West, where the McCormick *versus* Deering battle raged most fiercely, its strength had been less impaired by the rigor of savage competition. Its factory made disk, peg-tooth, and spring-tooth harrows, small cultivators, and hay tools, as well as the Osborne line of harvesting machinery. In the same year the Minnie Harvester plant was acquired in connection with an effort to make twine out of American flax, which was a natural product of the district around St. Paul.

In 1904, Harvester bought the little Keystone Company, of Rock Falls, Illinois, and thus acquired an historic line of tillage implements and hay tools to supply the Western trade. The Weber Wagon Company, of Chicago, was taken over and brought a popular wagon into the International fold. The Kemp manure spreader was purchased; and the Akron factories of the defunct Aultman-Miller Company were acquired. In all of these cases except Osborne the controlling reason was to gain an easy access to some line of new business. Osborne was of natural interest because of its availability, as an Eastern factory not far from Atlantic ports, in the drive to secure foreign trade.

In each of these cases the International Harvester Company acquired a going business, an equipped factory already in operation, a manufacturing and sales staff, and the goodwill of an established position in some portion at least of the territory. Of equal importance were the new avenues of activity it sought to develop for itself. To gain manufacturing economies, the Milwaukee Harvester line was moved to McCormick Works and the Plano machines were given a home at Deering. An improved version of the Kemp manure spreader and a companion type of wagon to the Weber were installed in the Plano home at West Pullman. Milwaukee was equipped to produce cream separators and stationary gasoline engines. The first of the Company's tractors were assembled in 1906 in Upper Sandusky, Ohio, where trucks and transmissions were provided for the Milwaukee-made stationary engines. The vacated Aultman-Miller shops at Akron were devoted to the preliminary production of a high-wheeled, air-cooled type of motor truck (known, perhaps satirically, as an 'auto buggy'). This had been designed to meet what was thought to be the farmer's demand for a motor vehicle of his own type, which, in recognition of what was deemed to be his preference, must be made as nearly like his horse-drawn buggy in appearance as possible.

Leaving until later a discussion of what this early excursion into the field of farm power meant to agriculture, it may be instructive to examine the broad significance of this reaching out into the new lines whose development was thus begun. The addition of cultivators and disk harrows meant that for the first time a business heretofore dedicated to the harvesting of a crop was to provide utensils whose business it was to explore beneath the surface of the ground. As plow-makers have learned to their sorrow, soil resistance varies from community to community and even within any given field. The problem of designing moving machinery to withstand stresses and strains that can be reasonably predicted in advance is difficult enough. It involves careful calculation and the long tests of experience to determine the relation of applied power and desired result. A plow or a cultivator, which has to do so much of its work in secret, is simpler by far in that it contains fewer moving parts; but a greater knowledge of the strength of materials is required. The robustness of design needed to withstand unexpected shocks was a lesson impressed later upon farm-implement makers by the necessity of dealing with the tractor's stream of tireless power; but the problem of work under the surface had its full share in teaching the International Harvester Company how better to strengthen its materials in terms of cultivating, plowing, listing, and the like.

Cream separators, stationary engines, and manure spreaders were an even better expression of non-harvesting experience. They led the Company directly into touch with activities in which the farmer engages for many months before and after the gathering of his crops. Manure spreaders taught a lesson of scientific farming wherein an agriculturist, by means of the provision of fertilizer, could draw more yield and therefore more profit from the soil. Cream separators opened a way to dairy worlds that were entirely set apart from wheat and which brought a different psychology into play on farm problems. The gasoline engine's object was to lighten labor, just as the reaper's had been; but its purpose was general and not specific. Available power would prove to be the key to unlock another door — that to the most modern type of agriculture.

And yet the reaper, just as it first solved the problem of farm labor, lay in the background behind these newer implements. There may seem to be a very slight connection between the reaper of 1831 and a modern manure spreader, less even between it and an engine whose fuel was undreamed of then, or a cream separator whose centrifugal object it is to replace the pan and ladle. The significant point is that it and they were both mechanisms which not only replaced labor, but functioned more efficiently. The reaper turned men's minds to the solution of farm labor problems. It started a train of thought that later was to bring into being so many mechanical answers to the farmer's needs.

Of greater importance to agriculture than these new machines was the element of stabilization brought to the industry by the formation of the International Harvester Company. Chaos had been reigning. The harvester war had started between McCormick and Hussey and then had raged between McCormick and Manny. For a time the protagonists had been McCormick and Champion. Most recently it had been a struggle, apparently to the death, between McCormick and Deering. Always the ancient leader had been forging on ahead, always there had been some one to challenge its aggressiveness. The net result of constant turmoil was disaster — for the manufacturer, for the local agent, for the farmer. The last had frequently enjoyed the benefit of low prices if the turn of battle should happen to take the form of price-cutting competition; but that was all. The farmer could not buy a machine from a manufacturer with any assurance that the vendor would be in existence next year. The maker could not have the benefit of a great volume of foreign sales to increase his production and thereby reduce his costs and his selling price. Above all, the farmer could not under the old system get the benefit of the large sums the Harvester Company immediately began to spend each year in organized experimental research.

American business men now believe that uncertainty is the worst of all commercial evils. If business is to be good, they can provide for it; if bad, they can prepare for it; and if it is to be normal, they can surround the conduct of their affairs with some assurance for the future. In the case of the International Harvester Company, this assurance of stabilized conditions rather than chaos took the form of a more intensified understanding of the purveying of necessities of life. Binders and mowers and gasoline engines and manure spreaders are not luxury articles.

They are basic necessities. People do not buy necessities because they want to, but because they have to. For a luxury they will pay a long price and make no complaint; but they will deliberate over the terms of a necessary transaction and demand those things they feel they have a right to expect.

The most vital desideratum in the eyes of purchasers is service. What investigation of the field problems has the manufacturer made to insure a potential customer that the article in question will meet his needs? What service can the seller render to facilitate selection? What assurance can the maker or the wholesaler or the retailer give of instruction in the use of the new device or of adjustment in its after life? These are questions which any vendor of a necessity must expect from any purchaser. It cannot be written into the purchase contract that the resulting functions will be performed. But customer goodwill is the most productive of all investments. People in general and farmers in particular were soon to learn that they could expect more worth from the plans and efforts of the new company than they had ever been able to receive from its weaker component parts. Their problems were its problems. Its success was theirs.

CHAPTER VIII

THE EARLY HARVESTER COMPANY YEARS

IT IS probable that the deeper evils resulting from the great harvester war were not appreciated at the time of the formation of the International Harvester Company. Of these, by no means the least was the decline of the trade in the old-line harvesting machines which, as has been shown, had been forced by undue competition to a volume far larger than the normal farm demand could sustain. As soon as the managers of the consolidation realized this, they sought to secure relief by attacking the problems of so-called vertical integration through company production of raw materials and by expansion through the development of new lines of product.

It has been related how the Deering Company bought land on the Calumet River in South Chicago and planned to erect blast furnaces. It fell to the International Harvester Company to develop this property. It had been proposed to produce some sixty-five thousand tons of steel a year; but now the demands for Company-made steel were greater and additional equipment was provided nearly to double the estimated production. The making of steel is a grimy business, full of the din of continuing utility and the nerve-tension of never-ending demand. It is also romantic with accomplishment. To get an adequate volume for production, much more steel had to be made than the Company itself required; and the disposal of this surplus has become a useful contribution to Harvester's widening field of sales.

The development of the Deering ore leases on the Mesaba Range and of the coal lands in Kentucky followed after the organization of the new company. The exploitation of the ore mines was a picturesque tale of industrial conquest. The coal fields were sixty miles away from a railway. But the solution of apparently difficult problems was not too much for the heirs of men who had moved Deering Works overnight or who had rebuilt McCormick Works so splendidly after the Chicago Fire. The railroad was persuaded to bring in its tracks, beehive coke ovens were constructed, coal veins were opened, and a new town in the Kentucky hills was built. This little city, planned in terms of the new science of welfare, was one of Harvester's first efforts at providing twentieth-century surroundings for workmen.

At Hamilton, Ontario, a new plant was begun in 1903 on land which the provident Deerings had purchased. The Canadian duty on agricultural implements had never been heavy; but they had wished to gain such small advantage as they could. In those days the benefits of quantity production were not understood; so it is not surprising that they expected, by having a Canadian factory, to save the entire duty. The International Harvester Company determined to manufacture there its Canadian requirements of binders, mowers, and such other machines as were built especially for the Canadian market.

The effort to develop a flax twine industry in the Minnie Harvester plant at St. Paul was unsuccessful. Although the technical processes were perfected, the science and skill of the United States Government, the State agricultural authorities, and the International Harvester Company could not make a twine which, when bound neatly around a sheaf of grain, would repel the appetite of grasshoppers. The soft flax became their favorite diet; so the Company perforce wrote off more

than a million dollar loss and had to admit that the
experiment was a failure. Flax, for which so much had
been expected, could not be used as a commercially satisfactory binder-twine material. Twine production was,
therefore, confined to hard fiber bought in Yucatan and
the Philippines, which was spun in the twine mills at
McCormick, Deering, Auburn, and St. Paul.

However disastrous may have been the Harvester
Company's effort to provide binder twine made of
American-grown flax, its other efforts to help the farmer
by producing new lines of usable tools were more successful. The greater part of the money spent on the
manufacturing establishment went toward the equipping
of the new-line factories. The modernization of the old
harvesting-machine plants simply had to wait. Cream
separator and stationary engine manufacture was installed at Milwaukee in place of the former line of harvesting machinery which had been removed to McCormick Works. A great new gray iron foundry was built,
the largest in the Company and one of the largest in the
world. But the new era of the factory did not really start
until 1908, when tractor production began, although
Milwaukee was making the power plants for the Company's Upper Sandusky-made tractors as early as 1906.
The Auburn, Akron, Springfield, West Pullman, and
Rock Falls shops were enlarged.

The distribution of product between these many plants
was entirely scientific and logical. The manufacture of
any given machine was centralized in one factory, except
as concerned Auburn and Rock Falls Works, where a
freight differential on business designed for the East and
South or for the West governed the allocation of product.
The resulting manufacturing economies were, however,
nowhere near important enough to affect sales prices.

Then, too, wages and the cost of purchased materials kept on increasing and counteracted the first efforts at efficiency; and the demand for the old-line harvesting machines failed to return to the former level. Nevertheless, the Company's manufacturing program was aided by the new business secured abroad and in the new-line products. They were providing the economic justification for the consolidation and the resulting exploration into new fields of endeavor. Thus, by 1912 the Company was spending twice as much for production labor as in 1902. No one of the factories was less active than ten years before, no line of manufacture had been abandoned, and many new articles had been introduced for the first time.

McCormick and Deering Works went on very much as before. They each had famous records as producing centers for harvesting machinery, and it is perhaps the fault of this fame, which they themselves had justified, that their new entities demanded so little of the large sums the Company was spending for new and revised production equipment. Their former manufacturing leadership had been outstanding. The seeds of mass production had been sown in the first McCormick Works before 1850; and the Deering Company had, by 1902, taken important early steps toward the integration of raw materials and demand. Their great foundries and their novel molding machinery were the admiration of the iron world. Their records for low-cost production were remarkable. They were the wonder of nineteenth-century manufacturing. Their novel fragments of modern mass-production methods, their mower-frame boring machines and section-hardening furnaces were still abreast of the times. The salesmen of those days were even able to make and prove the surprising assertion that the price of a grain binder with its hundreds of moving parts was less per pound than that of an ordinary domestic cook stove.

McCormick and Deering Works had gone far in a world that had not quite discovered mass production. And yet the Harvester Company, in spite of all its growing resources, was unable to expand its trade facilities all over the world, provide enough capital to equip so many new production enterprises, and at the same time keep abreast in all particulars with the pace of twentieth-century progress. The old factories lost none of their former excellence nor their ability to produce agricultural implements at a cost which was — and is — the envy of the manufacturing world. But it must be admitted that they did not readily accept the new theories of mass-production methods which between 1910 and 1915 were being tried out in the newest automobile factories. Thus, even Tractor Works, built after 1910 and devoted though it was to the construction of the Company's most modern machine, the tractor, bore only a slight resemblance to what would now be considered a mass-production shop. Harvester's ability to produce had not weakened, but it was not developing as fast as were the manufacturing systems of other industries. Where the motor-car world was beginning to progress with new ideas and new methods, International's harvesting-machine and new-line factories had for the present to forgo modernization. Circumstances had compelled the Harvester Company to devote its capital and energies to selling the new lines, to raw material properties, and to the fostering of the export business.

At the time the Harvester Company was being formed, the rising protective tariffs of foreign countries threatened exclusion from foreign markets already developed

at great expense and by years of effort.   It was therefore
determined to embark upon a broad course of foreign
manufacture.   The first of the European plants established was the Swedish Works at Norrkoping in 1905.
The initial production consisted largely of mowers, with
other implements and twine following as a matter of
course, as the high Swedish duties made it desirable to
produce that country's requirements within its borders.
In 1909, a site for a German factory was chosen at Neuss,
due consideration being given to the superfine manufacturing facilities of the Rhineland and to the remarkable German distributing system of canals and railways.
Old factories were purchased at Croix, near Lille, in
northeastern France, and at Lubertzy, near Moscow, in
the heart of Russia.   The last was designed to produce
the *lobogreika*, a Russian form of reaper suited to the
unsophisticated state of agriculture in that mysterious
country.   The French and German factories were prepared to produce a general line of harvesting and tillage
tools and binder twine.

The first decade of Harvester Company experience was
devoted to an active and progressive interest in the development of human relations.   In the earlier years of the
twentieth century, a very few industrial organizations
sought to discover those elements in industrial relations
which made for better work and more contented workers.
The United States Steel Corporation, for example, easily
assumed an outstanding leadership in the cause of safety.
In later years the International Harvester Company was
to command the field of forward-looking companies that
concern themselves with the investigation and solution of
personnel problems.   In its youth it was equally a leader
in the field of welfare.

Let me emphasize that the difference between industrial welfare policies of, say, 1910, and the understanding of industrial relations policies that exists to-day, is profound. It may possibly be compared to the difference between a feudalistic state — the government of which, however enlightened, contains nothing of the consent of the governed — and a democracy. It is not suggested that an industrial democracy needs to, or does, resemble a political democracy; but it is certainly true, that if people have a voice in the making of the regulations which affect them, they are more able to understand and accept law. The world attained democracy only after passing through a stage of feudalism. Similarly, the world of business attained the modern system of industrial relations, which is so largely based upon democratic principles of conduct, after an experimental period of welfare.

I say this because I am proud of the fact that the International Harvester Company was one of the first large industrial companies to lead the way to welfare and thus take a radical step in the direction of industrial relations. It seems to me that the lot of the great body of the workmen in the older harvester factories cannot formerly have been the happiest. I once heard my grandmother and my mother talk longingly of the hoped-for flower beds and grass which now adorn the front yard at McCormick Works; and I have seen some of the pre-International sanitary installations which later knowledge has replaced with more adequate facilities. If the McCormick and Deering workmen were once provided with washrooms which would seem lamentably insufficient to modern eyes, they enjoyed far better working conditions than the men in the out-of-Chicago factories which came into the International Harvester Company, or those in other factories in the city. To arrive, it is necessary to start.

It must be remembered that before 1900 there was a great deal of strife between the supposedly hostile camps of capital and labor. Chicago had several times seen men shot down because of open revolt. A huge force of Pinkerton detectives was organized to protect factory property from riots growing out of strikes. After the Haymarket riots the political efforts of the Working-men's Party were crushed for a while, but in 1894 they revived, and President Cleveland had to call out troops to quell a bloody railway strike and prevent interference with the United States mails. Before 1902, wages throughout the Nation were low, although the effect of the early customs tariffs was being felt and they were rising. Both capital and labor had to learn first how to discover and then how to enjoy prosperity.

In 1912, when the Company was already a recognized leader in welfare work, the following advanced statement of policy was issued:

There was a period in the industrial development of this country when employers gave little or no attention to the physical or moral welfare of their employees. About the only thought that an employer had for his men was on the day the pay envelope had to be filled; and the employee's interest in his employer was aroused from its sub-normal condition to one of active concern when the paymaster hove in sight. Rapid strides away from this condition have been made in the past few years.... Many employers have come to realize that they owe more than the wages, and that their employees are entitled to clean, light, sanitary, and safe places in which to work, to compensation when disabled, and to provision for old age. A careful business man sees that his property is maintained in excellent condition.... Welfare work, so-called, is simply applying the same business principles to his employees that he applies to the rest of his business. Good welfare work, like good business, pays.

While this ideal is not entirely modern, in that it expresses what we would to-day consider a step in the right direction rather than the attainment of a sought-for ideal, it was far ahead of its time in 1912. The industrial world has, for example, heard much of the benefit of group and other insurance. In 1908, the International Harvester Company established an Employees' Benefit Association. This is a mutual society maintained by the Company's contribution of administration expenses, the employees' contributions going entirely to benefits. The Association relieves the minds of its members from financial worries when they cannot work because of sickness or of off-duty accident, and its provision for the widows and children of deceased Harvester men has been helpful. Incidentally the periodical factory elections for Association trustees provided, eleven years later, an excellent school of preparation for the exercise of the employee representation franchise.

Financial relief for accidents in the course of duty was provided for by a compensation plan adopted in 1910. The International Harvester Company was beginning to adopt a policy of voluntary liberalism and its plan assumed as a charge against itself the cost of all industrial accidents from whatever cause. A number of State compensation laws, subsequently passed, followed its terms. As fast as such legislation became effective, the Company substituted the State systems for its own previous scheme of voluntary compensation.

Matters affecting an employee's working conditions were vigorously studied. Guards were provided for moving machinery, books of rules for the avoidance of accidents were printed, and foremen gave instruction in safety. Until 1919 there were no works councils, so it was impossible before then to tap the greatest of all reservoirs of safety education, namely, the elected representatives of the men themselves. Nevertheless, the Harvester record for safety was impressive, and the Company was already well on its way to its present acknowledged leadership.

Some reference has been made to pre-1902 working conditions and their too-frequent insufficiency. Viewed with our educated perspective, they may not have been good; but that was so simply because manufacturers had not yet learned what influence environment could have on efficiency. Sanitation became the order of the day for Harvester before any other company began to study the subject. Old equipment was replaced, the drinking-fountain appeared, ventilating systems were installed, and the scientific application of electric lighting was studied. Even in its first years, the Company began to codify standards governing such matters. Exhaust systems were provided for grinding rooms and over emery wheels, first aid was practiced, factory hospitals were organized, and a matron was engaged wherever any number of women were working.

I do not pretend that what was accomplished before 1912 in the development of welfare, even the splendid forward step of prohibiting night work for women, was more than a good beginning. The manufacturing executives of the Company had been trained in a different, ruder school. Doubtless many of them did not appreciate, as did the higher management, the need for improvement in the application of welfare work; and their education may have seemed a slow matter. But a new generation of men was taking charge of the factories. The change in executive personnel due to promotion or resignation was rapid, and a younger generation was growing up to take the place of the stern veterans of the harvester war, who, simply because they themselves had survived, had every right to believe that the fittest men alone should be permitted to live on. The new men were advancing by great strides and were putting their company far in the lead among industrial concerns. They discussed such matters under the head of health, whereas we of to-day now consider them, and health as well, as the essential foundation of efficiency. But they accomplished much with practically nothing to begin with, and, under the leadership of Cyrus H. McCormick, they laid the sure foundation for the more developed science of the present years. When a future historian looks back on our generation's work, he will consider it good if we have made as much of an advance beyond previous standards as they did.

The most important of the early forward-looking policies adopted by the International Harvester Company was the establishment, in 1908, of a pension system. The plan was not the first in the industrial world; but its provisions were remarkable for their liberality. It was not announced to a group of young workingmen who would have to wait for a long period to enjoy its benefits, but was made immediately applicable to all employees. A fund was set aside from operating capital to insure an income for the constantly increasing amount of pension payments. The entire cost of pensions was — and is — borne by the Company, no contribution being made by the employee.

Many business organizations, stable enough to warrant an expectancy of continued existence, have since adopted pension schemes, but none has exceeded the provision for the future offered by this plan and its subsequent enlargements. Modern students say rightly that continuity of employment bulks largest in a workman's eyes when he considers working conditions. The second most important consideration is provision for his declining, unproductive years. Eager young men whose lives lie in the future may not concern themselves deeply over their last years; but stable workmen, whose best period may have been given to one task, cannot but worry as to what may happen to them when their strength declines. Many Harvester men had been on the pay roll for forty years or more. They had seen agricultural implements develop from crude origins into efficient machines. Too frequently they had seen their companies drifting toward a financial incompetency that meant the ending of all hope for themselves. Now they had been taken over into a strong family, able to look forward to the future. Furthermore, this new group looked at their affairs as human problems. The day had gone when an employee was merely a machine with legs and arms. He had aspirations which should and could be recognized. The Harvester Company flatly propounded the doctrine that provision for these wants was a charge, not upon the isolated individual, but upon the entire business.

Such a radical departure from what would once have been considered the accepted conservatism of capitalism was entirely consistent with the enlightened McCormick tradition. If one examines carefully the life of the inventor of the reaper, one may easily discover more of a tolerance toward the problems of humanity than one might expect from a dominant, assertive, ruthless business man. In the case of his son, leader now of wider destinies, the father's dominant will was muted to self-control; and devotion to the cause of the reaper had become a willingness — an eagerness — to recognize the rights of others.

It has been said that the world has ever been able to discover the right leader when an emergency appears.

Cyrus Hall McCormick was such a man for the development of the reaper, a pioneer in a time when pioneering was needed, who could thrust a way through the barriers obstructing the road to the future. Cyrus H. McCormick, his son, was temperamentally able to lead the International Harvester Company through its first, difficult years and turn suspicion into faith. It would have been too much to expect all Deering men, all McCormick men, and all the men of the other organizations, factory men and salesmen alike, to accept one another wholeheartedly simply because their former families had been scrambled. But if it was difficult for some of these old warriors to yield to the fact of consolidation, it was, conversely, impossible for the president of the new family to accept anything less than ultimate harmony and coordination as the standard of his organization.

In all his efforts he was ably seconded by his brother Harold and by Alexander Legge, who became general manager when C. S. Funk, of Champion, resigned in 1913 to become president of the Rumely Company. He had won his way upward through every rank, and, since he was one of those men to whom problems and difficulties are the meat and drink of existence, the things he learned in each stage of his progress became capital in the bank of his advancement. Possessed of a fiery, forceful temperament, he could inspire men by his vigorous vision, compel them to success by the power of his own example, work himself with a never-ending consecration, and make other men want to work. He and his president gave the new company exactly the touch needed to prove to the world that the thrill of perseverance and vision and the ultimate success of well-laid plans were not the dead attributes of the age of romance. They proved that high ideals could be a measure of practical existence.

ALEXANDER LEGGE

HAROLD F. McCORMICK

In 1912, Cyrus H. McCormick wrote of the Company's first ten years:

The International Harvester Company has attempted to show that a large corporation can be directed and inspired by the same high ideals which so often characterize the management of a private business. It has not tried to shield its actions behind any impersonal forms, but has accepted the full responsibility for its acts, and has asked to be judged by what it does. Its officers and leading employees have spent their lives in building up a sound and creditable business organization, and their purpose and effort have been to bring to this Company the same personal zeal for honorable success which gave to the predecessor companies the high esteem of the commercial world.

However popular the old companies had been with the farming public, there can be no question that by 1912 the new consolidation was even higher in favor with the agricultural world. Farmers had come to look to it for service in their interests; and they had come to realize that Harvester men were actuated by something more than a mere desire to make and sell implements. Harvester men had received from Harvester history a deep inspiration which knit them in the common cause of service. They became imbued with a spirit, a force that permitted and compelled them to carry on.

It is difficult to define an abstract quality; and in the case of Harvester Spirit, it would be simpler to relate the annals of Harvester men and thus set forth a living picture of its workings. In truth, it has so taken possession of their consciousness that their every occupation is an expression of its qualities. Individually, it is a very personal force leading men on to accomplishment. Collectively, it is a bond that knits them into a strong union for a common purpose. Its result has been that sincere and constructive urge to serve which made it impossible for Harvester men, great or small, to treat employees or customers unfairly. It has woven the many thousands of them into one family, so to speak — a personal association dedicated to an ideal. This ideal has been the effective personalization of the cause of service to the farmer.

It is said that in Rockbridge County, Virginia, even before 1831, Robert McCormick and his family, obviously among the chief citizens in that rural community, lived somewhat apart from their neighbors. The other farmers and villagers may have felt that Robert and his wife and his eldest son were inspired by a different, wider intellectual vigor. When the young inventor grew beyond his father's stature, he made the whole body of farmers members of his mental family; and he considered his and their common purpose more worth while than the activities of other men. No matter how, in later life, he may have come to be respected as an industrialist, as a leading citizen, as a man of wealth, or as a churchman, he himself felt that his distinction rested on his self-dedication to the cause of agriculture. This was what he had sought in the highways and byways of life — he wanted the esteem of the farmers to be his chief memorial.

The tradition he established lived after him and flourished. How many times I have heard Alex Legge, first among Harvester men of that day and this, tell of how my grandmother summoned a visiting general agent to her house to tell her of the state of business on the far frontiers, and how that man would later return to the office fired with her zeal. How often I have seen Harvester men pay tribute to my father's principles by adopting them as their own. He had piloted his company through a soul-testing period when every ounce of his wisdom and his strength of purpose were needed, and out of which the organization came with the mature vigor of tried and true devotion. As president of the International Harvester Company, his courage, fairness, and determination were a shining example to men who might otherwise have sought to continue within the consolidation the warfare of the past. He and his brother Harold could set such an example because they, too, had dedicated their lives to the advancement of agriculture. They were living in terms of a practical ideal which could not be achieved except by the upright activities of the thousands whom they were teaching, as their father had taught them, to serve the farmer.

With the exception of a few, the old leaders who had formed the International Harvester Company had dropped out of active operations by the time the first ten years were run. Executive positions were being filled by the younger McCormick managers, by the junior Deering men to whom the struggles of the past had not been so acute, by a scattering of promoted Champion and Keystone executives, and by a constantly increasing number of individuals who had had no previous connection with Harvester affairs. One and all, these men were won by the living force of the old tradition. Its vigor enveloped them and in their hands became Harvester Spirit. They solidified the Harvester family, they kept Harvester Spirit intact through the years of trial, they handed it on to the younger generation.

They could not have done so if this spirit had not been to a certain extent self-propagating. An ideal of service is ever strong. This one was sure enough to weld the men of many organizations into one group, to pass from them into new groups of younger Harvester men and cause them also to be coherent in an even finer way. Harvester Spirit has grown as much out of the dedicated minds of the thousands of Harvester men all over the world as from the ideals of their chiefs. They and the things they do are its best expression. When a branch manager will arise at midnight from his yearned-for bed to open the warehouse and get a farmer a harvester knotter spring which costs five cents and upon which that farmer's entire harvest depends, he is actuated by something more than a desire to hold his job. A factory laborer who lends his shoulder to another's task is spending himself for agriculture. The local dealers and the legion of farmers who have learned to trust a corporation for service — they are echoing the subtle influence of Harvester Spirit. In far-away New Zealand I have seen the same fighting determination energizing a group of men no one of whom has ever visited the parent source of inspiration in Chicago.

There is nothing secret, nothing occult, in Harvester Spirit. Justice, fairness, truth, the right at all times at whatever cost — these were the ideals by which a growing commercial organism was actuated. The men of the new Harvester generation felt these things because they lived by them. At the top of the organization, proudly planning for its further expansion, were leaders like Couchman, H. F. Perkins, Utley, and Ranney of the McCormick staff; McKinstry and Haney of Deering; Edgar of Champion; and Johnston of Keystone. Many new men like Reay, the comptroller, and a hundred others brought in to strengthen the ranks of enlarging departments, became imbued with the modern force of ancient ideals. I have heard Alex Legge attribute Harvester Spirit to my father's influence; but I think his praise is too broad. The credit for making it effective, and for the presence in a commercial organization of practical ideals which are usually supposed to be the crown of private life alone, belongs to all Harvester men.

CHAPTER IX

THE TRANSITION TO MODERN MACHINERY

AT THE formation of the International Harvester Company, the constituent organizations made nothing more than harvesting machinery. All five of them made grain binders, the leading implement of the agricultural world, reapers, corn binders, mowers, and hay rakes. McCormick, Deering, and Plano also manufactured the push type of harvester, the large machine used in the West, and its companion, the header, a favorite implement in the dry-farming districts which deposited the loose heads in an accompanying wagon to be hauled away to await the threshing process. The two larger companies also manufactured the corn husker and shredder; Champion made a very few hay tedders; and Osborne, at the time it became a part of the new company, was the leading producer of this tool.

These machines, with knife grinders, constitute what are called the 'old lines.' Immediately after the amalgamation, Harvester, as has been said, turned its attention to an intensive development of 'new lines.' These included various machines which were acquired because they already enjoyed an established reputation, such as the Osborne series of tillage implements, the Keystone hay tool and corn sheller line, the Weber wagon and the Kemp manure spreader. They also comprised the developments pioneered by Harvester's own experimental effort, such as corn pickers, cream separators, stationary engines, tractors, and the embryo motor truck. For a time, also, even pleasure motor cars were assembled, but this precarious venture was of short duration. By 1912, hay presses, seeding machinery, corn planters, and ensilage cutters had also been put on the market. The first harvester-thresher appeared in 1914, and the stationary thresher in 1918.

Trade in the new lines has through the years assumed a constantly increasing importance to the Company's economic position. In 1903, it amounted to but a twentieth part of the entire business. In 1916, the new-line volume for the first time exceeded the old; and as the war-born demand for tractors came to be felt, it jumped far in the lead. It may not be out of place to say that at present the old lines constitute less than ten per cent of the sales volume. The supremacy of the old harvesting lines has passed.

The 'full line' which the International Harvester Company was developing could not be completed until after 1918 when plows were added to its number of machines; but even before then the catalogue included an enormous variety of implements. By that year the line of seven or eight original harvesting tools had so broadened as to include almost every type of horse-drawn machine a farmer need for crop production except plows. After the sod or stubble had been broken, the cycle of the Company's interest in the farmer's workaday activities began. There were harrows of every type to smooth the turned furrows, grain drills for seeding, and planters for corn or cotton. There were cultivators and a variety of other tools for tending the growing crops, and a multitude of harvesting implements for reaping grain or corn in every way desired by any special locality. There were threshing machines and the early models of the harvester-thresher, that most efficient of all modern farm implements which cuts grain and threshes it in a single operation. There were mowers, many kinds of rakes, tedders, and loaders in sufficient variety to suit the many climatic and other conditions under which hay is grown; corn pickers, shellers, huskers, and ensilage cutters; wagons and motor trucks for hauling; cream separators for the dairyman and stationary engines for the small farm or the municipal power plant; and there were tractors.

Most of these many machines were designed originally, or were sooner or later redesigned from their former types, by the Company itself. Research and experimental work were organized immediately after the amalgamation. Under the old companies, the owner of the competing business himself had charge of this work. Once his business began to grow, the inventor of the reaper had to give over the duty of designing to others, but he never lost interest in progress and development. The annals of McCormick, of Deering, and of the other warriors of the old days are full of stories of the search for new devices, of days and nights spent in the fields testing an idea against the sternest demands of actual use, and of the glamor of final success retrieved from the very portal of failure. After 1902, the heads of the business had to concern themselves with problems of administration and weighty matters of policy; so from the mechanical staffs of the former companies they gathered a group of inventors and other men whose genius was born out of experience in the study and solution of the farmer's mechanical problems.

Modern experimental work is not as spectacular as it was in 1831, because it so frequently must concern itself with the more detailed problems brought into being by specialization and because, too often, it is anonymous. In the old days, when the world of machinery was new, great ideas seemed to spring full-blown from the brain of a genius. We, who perhaps fear that we must travel over trodden paths, fail to realize how insufficient, judged by our sophisticated standards, was the work of men like Fulton or McCormick or Morse. Surely, though, there is much credit for the man of to-day who attacks a problem because he is told to do so, who works at his drawing board because it is his duty and not simply because of a divine urge within him to create, who tries — and who succeeds.

Practically never does his first plan work. He must throw away what he has done, keep the lesson of his first failure, try again. Always he has to keep in his mind the commercial requirements of his task. There is a cream separator to design, for example. Such a device is nothing new; it has long since been stripped of its mystery and reduced to formulas of rotation, gravity, and the strength of materials; and it is admitted that there is something wrong with every previous effort of other men whose experience may have seemed to canonize their work. Then, too, whatever he does must stand the cold analysis of sales judgment and accountancy, which will say that such and such are the requirements of a dairy farmer, and that if the price of the machine exceeds a certain figure, the prospective customer will refuse to buy. Finally, there are so many men to please. But ever there is a chance to shorten the hours of farm labor, increase production, or reduce the cost of farm products.

New design is not the only problem. I have heard it said that science marches ahead so quickly into unexplored fields of intellectual endeavor, or finds so many flaws in deductions gained from previous knowledge, that the scientist of 1900 would be but a beginner if he had not kept on growing between that time and this. Similarly, even the tried and true grain binders of 1902 have since been worked over and changed to keep them up to date and efficient in relation to the constantly enlarging requirements of agriculture. An archaic type of machine was deemed good in its day because men knew no better when it was first offered to them; but out of it has grown experience. Experience involves standards for former methods as much as the critical ability to value new processes. The International Harvester Company bought well-established and honorable trade names for tillage tools, hay tools, wagons, and spreaders. Nevertheless, it soon found the necessity of changing and improving those machines if they were to be kept worthy of the new cream separators, engines, tractors, and motor trucks which were constantly appearing.

When the standards governing implement specifications are in process of formation, new types of machinery are carried south to the earliest harvest district and started north in the train of the ripening grain. This is arduous, but it gives several years' experience in one summer; and it is infinitely preferable to the primitive method of McCormick in Virginia, where, if he failed to correct a given difficulty, he could have no further chance of doing so until next year. Gradually, the relation of moving parts and the equations governing such things as the strength of materials were reduced to a science. This science lies only in men's minds, for no volume can hold the text of experience, and agricultural implement engineering has to deal with too many variables for ready classification. One designs a binder or a mower in the field or by night over the forge of a country blacksmith shop, not from the published data of mathematical formulas. The designing of farm machinery demands an intimate knowledge of farm psychology as well as farm economics.

When the tractor was growing up, the empirical

method of implement engineering could to a certain extent be supplemented by the documented evidence which grew out of automobile designing. A tractor is made of materials so expensive that their every qualification must be known. The manufacturing limits can and must be expressed to a nicety. The results to be expected from horse-power and gear ratios can be predicted in advance and subsequently checked with absolute assurance. But a tractor, which is purposeless if it is not able to work at all times under maximum stresses and strains, is not an easy problem. An automobile does not have to run at top speed for every minute of its productive life, an airplane engine is always in the hands of the most skilled mechanics to check or repair any incipient ill. The tractor has to work — it has to be designed for never-ending toil, for the task of furnishing available, immediate, and dependable farm power.

The work of reconditioning the old lines and providing a complete assortment of new-line equipment would have been difficult enough for any group of engineers. Under the Harvester Company plan of distribution, with at least one McCormick and one Deering dealer in every town, the engineers were asked to provide two designs of each machine. As the so-called full line developed, it became necessary to supply each of these sales agents with a complete assortment of implements to accompany the line-leading binder in order to round out the field of his trade possibilities. Each of these secondary tools had to be different from, and yet had to perform as satisfactorily as, its brother. Thus gradually through the years there came into being an enormous variety of machinery which taxed the engineers to plan and the factories to manufacture. There were, for example, two complete sets of tillage implements, at least two manure spreaders, two wagons, two cream separators, two types of stationary engines, and for a time at least there were two tractor lines.

I am not sure that this was entirely a sound plan. In the early years of the Company, it was apparently the intention to provide a multiple series of machines to accompany the six harvester lines; and an attempt was even made to provide a special binder for the Keystone tillage line. Thus, a few header-harvesters were made after 1906 for Champion, and side-delivery rakes and tedders were added to the McCormick and Deering lines. The endeavor was futile and fell of its own weight. One sales organization could not stretch its attention to so many almost identical machines of the same class. Then, too, after 1912, the McCormick and Deering lines became, by popular selection, the leading Harvester Company products. When I was on the sales force in 1915 and 1916, we found some trouble in disposing of the lesser lines — although in certain localities a dealer would accept no other.

It required some planning to deal satisfactorily with the double sales arrangements imposed upon us by the double McCormick and Deering lines. We had to be prepared to propound the advantages of each — and I think that I, although of the house of McCormick, was impartial between the two. Yet all our efforts did not greatly change their relative standing. McCormick and Deering binder sales in the United States were very nearly equal in 1903 and very nearly equal for the first twenty International years; and Deering mower sales never approximated more than three-quarters of McCormick. In the foreign field the early McCormick ascendency had established a name for itself that kept it always slightly in the lead.

But the great day of the harvesting machine as a leader of the Company's business was over. New times had brought new and better methods to the agricultural equipment world. The tractor had been born and it was rapidly replacing the horse as a measure of farm power. The story of the early progress of power farming is a long one and cannot be told here in its entirety. Suffice it to say that the invention of the tractor was almost as important to the farmer as the invention of the reaper.

As a matter of fact, both the reaper and the tractor are similar in their object. The social importance of the reaper was that it substituted horse-power for the tired muscles of straining peasants; the social importance of the tractor is that it substitutes mechanical power for those tasks which sap the strength of men and animals. Both brought the power of machinery to the aid of man. Both presented a way of accomplishing a desired result with less body-racking, soul-testing effort. Progressively they freed men's minds from the apparent delusion of necessity: and then presented an opportunity for work with brains as a better substitute for work with brawn. Power farming really began to appear in 1831 with the invention of the reaper. Its story is perhaps not yet finished, even with the twentieth century and the invention of the tractor.

The difference between the reaper and the tractor as examples of applied power is but a matter of degree. It is certainly true that material progress must be valued in terms of preceding and surrounding circumstances. The invention of the reaper would have been unimportant if it had followed the introduction of the harvester-thresher. The reaper is remarkable because it was the first machine to summon the then almost unknown capacity of mechanics to the relief of manual agriculture. The tractor, master to-day of a farmer's power problems, is a direct descendant in the original strain of power application and labor elimination. It has grown out of the reaper just as surely as the automobile has risen from the first wheeled chariot. Man's experience and wisdom could not in 1831 produce a tractor; but they could not avoid producing the ancestor of the tractor, the reaper.

The story of the tractor properly begins with the discovery of steam. Watt's patent of 1784 was for a steam road carriage, not for the railway locomotive which Stephenson produced in 1817 as a better substitute for the engine of the highways. The first portable steam power plant was built in Philadelphia in 1849. A year later, Horace Greeley wrote: 'The time must be at hand when every thrifty farmer will have such an engine of his own, and chopping straw, turning grindstone, cutting wood, churning, threshing, etc., will cease to be a manual and become a mechanical operation. ... This engine will be running on wheels and driving a scythe before it or drawing a plow behind it within five years. — We have hardly begun to use steam as yet.' In 1867, the United States Commissioner of Agriculture pointed out that power could be as helpful to farming as to transportation in that 'insufficient power with light plows breaks imperfectly a shallow depth, while the mighty power of steam, harnessed to strong implements, breaking, pulverizing, or intermixing soils, accomplishes all results of a superior cultivation in less time and at less expense than any other method.'

For many years the application of steam power to farm problems went no further than threshing, and the adaptation of power to plowing was not attempted until near the end of the nineteenth century. Even then the engines with which plowing was first attempted were power plants devised for threshing, movable only for purposes of transportation from field to field. When specially designed steam apparatus was produced, it was not successful. The field locomotive was too cumbersome and too costly for individual farm use.

The solution of the problem of the tractor lay in the Otto internal combustion engine of 1876. When the Otto patents ran out in 1890, so many companies in different parts of the world leaped into motor activity that by 1899 there were over a hundred kinds of four-cycle engines on the market. To-day they are all nameless, for, with the exception of Otto, who pioneered the original process and its theoretical background, no single inventor can be credited with the discovery of the gas engine. Otto's name may, if you will, be added to those of Whitney and McCormick to make up the trio whose practical researches have for all time been of the greatest benefit to farmers; but Otto was interested in power and in the functioning of his device as a prime mover for all purposes, not in agricultural power as such. The tractor of to-day derives its heritage more directly from the possibly many unnamed individuals who, for and by themselves, mounted stationary gasoline engines on movable frames.

What is supposed to be the first manufactured gasoline tractor dates from 1895; but this outfit stalled itself in a newly plowed field and, when it was finally extricated by half the community, it balked. During the next several years various individuals sought more or less ineffectually to build farm tractors. These efforts were directed to produce belt-power machines rather than tractors for plowing and other mobile work. It required the indirect impetus of the rapidly developing automobile industry, which by 1901 was producing some eighteen thousand motor cars a year, to spur enthusiasts for power farming into a realization of the scope of the field which lay before them.

The most noteworthy among the parents of the internal combustion tractor were two young engineers, C. W. Hart and C. H. Parr, of Charles City, Iowa. In the winter of 1901, they built a cumbersome two-cylinder, oil-cooled, slow-speed, two-cycle tractor which, sold during the following summer to an Iowa farmer, astonished all concerned by its ability to operate. The next year the two men constructed fifteen more tractors. That these early machines, crude though they may have been, were sound and serviceable is indicated by the surprising statement that in 1920 half of this first crop of farm tractors were still in the hands of farmer owners and still in operation.

Comparatively few tractors were built by any one before 1906, when the large-scale tractor industry was born. Western Canada was then being rapidly developed, the ultimate frontier of the agricultural United States had not been quite attained, and everywhere countless weary miles of plodding were awaiting farmers if they could find no substitute for the horse-drawn plow. Farmers were demanding general purpose motive power. There were no more than five hundred tractors in use upon American and Canadian farms when simultaneously eleven companies, including International Harvester, began the manufacture of tractors.

The first machines of the Harvester Company were equipped with a Milwaukee-made fifteen horse-power plant mounted on a friction drive chassis produced by the Ohio Manufacturing Company at Upper Sandusky, Ohio. The engine had an open crankcase, a single cylinder, make-and-break ignition, and spray tank cooling.

The whole power plant was shifted on rollers to engage the friction drive disk. Twenty-five of these crude machines were built and distributed to the territory for observation. The reports on their behavior were satisfactory, so in the following year two hundred were put out. But soon it became apparent that friction would not serve as a method of transmission; and when tractor manufacture was transferred in 1908 from Akron, where it had been housed for a time, to the larger Milwaukee Works, the standard type of geared transmission was adopted.

Mechanical plowing was then as essential to the development of western Canada as the reaper had been to the prairies across the Mississippi. The world's cry for bread was insistent, population was lacking, and, even though the resources of mechanized farm equipment were marshaled, the task of turning acres of prairie sod was too great. Saskatchewan and Alberta were measured in leagues, not in miles, and their huge farms extended beyond the horizon. Canadian interest in gaining a mechanical substitute for animal power was therefore keen. The first of the many great tractor plowing demonstrations was held at Winnipeg in the summer of 1908. Five manufacturers of gasoline tractors and five adherents of steam competed. Kinnard-Haines won, Harvester placed second, and the ultimate doom of steam was sounded. The net result of the test was that public interest was aroused, the mechanical weakness of existing designs was indicated, and a demand for equipment large enough to suit the conditions of western Canada became apparent.

Canada was then the leading tractor market, consuming over two-thirds of all tractors built and governing the type by its requirements. There was a second Winnipeg contest in 1909 and a third in 1910, both of which marked the trend toward increasing size. Where Harvester's first machines had been equipped with a modest fifteen horse-power engine, its two victorious 1909 entries developed twenty and twenty-five horse-power, and its 1910 model was of forty-five horse-power. Tractor design was improving, as evidenced by a decrease in the average weight per horse-power of the contestants from 537 pounds in 1908 to 504 pounds in 1910; but if we may judge by the standards of to-day, the machines were huge and lumbering. They ground their way slowly across the long field, cutting a wide furrow with as many as fifteen plow bottoms. This was the way western Canada wanted its sod turned.

The 1910 demonstration marked the first surrender of steam to gasoline and also the first appearance of kerosene as a fuel. For a time the threshermen fought against internal combustion. There are tales of bitter hand-to-hand combats; but their opposition was of no avail. Their ranks began to break when Rumely deserted steam and produced 'Kerosene Annie,' whose approach to Winnipeg was celebrated by a flaring advertising campaign which did more to capture popular attention for the tractor than a dozen shows.

The International Harvester Company climbed ahead of Hart-Parr as the leading producer in 1910, and by 1911 was responsible for perhaps a third of the United States output. In 1912, it made over three thousand tractors, followed by Rumely with nearly as many, and by Hart-Parr. Public interest seemed to center solely in the biggest machines. At the Winnipeg show in 1912, the average brake horse-power of the contestants exceeded fifty. Editorial writers clamored for small tractors; the American trade was becoming important and American farms were smaller than Canadian; engineers dreamed of small power units — but the public seemed to want nothing but the largest, heaviest machine possible. Harvester would have preferred to refine its original fifteen and twenty horse-power models rather than to explore an uncertain way into the sphere of magnitude where it had no experience. But it was helpless in the face of the demand. Thus, when Tractor Works was built in Chicago in 1910, the first buildings resembled a locomotive shop more than an implement works. The Company's position in the industry was based on the sale of many comparatively inexpensive implements to many farmers; but now its leading tractor was a sixty horse-power monster that weighed eleven tons. Its chief publicity stunt was to link three of these huge engines together and, pulling fifty-five plows, to turn a furrow sixty-four feet wide.

True to its traditions, the Harvester Company no sooner found itself in the tractor business than it began to seek to develop exports. In 1908, one of the early machines was shipped to France and one to Australia. The French machine competed at Amiens with a number of European makes and was victorious. Apparently its performance astounded the spectators, for the manager of the Paris office wrote, 'I am pleased to say that our tractor worked two complete days without stopping for a single instant owing to any defect or disarrangement of the working parts.' Soon International tractors appeared also in Russia, Austria, Mexico, and the Argentine. Russian wheat farms were huge, not unlike those of western Canada, and the tractor received a ready welcome. Plowing with three yoke of oxen to each bottom was tedious and expensive, and the larger landowners were eager for relief. Nevertheless, it may well be imagined

INTERNATIONAL HARVESTER TRACTOR SHOWN AT AMIENS,
FRANCE, 1909

THREE INTERNATIONAL HARVESTER TRACTORS PULLING
FIFTY-FIVE PLOW-BOTTOMS

that the cost of the monster tractors then in vogue was high and that distance and inexperience made efficient repair and expert service almost impossible. The wonder of it is that any company was so easily able to distribute tractors in the distant quarters of the globe.

The big tractor phase collapsed of its own weight. It may be presumed that the power needs of large farmers, hitherto accustomed to huge steam outfits, had required such a type. But the sixty horse-power giant demanded too much attention, too much skill in operation. Too many farmers, following the fashion, bought powerful machines for which they had no practical use. In 1914, there was a partial crop failure and many purchasers were unable to meet the deferred payments, which necessarily had to be so much larger than the sums they were accustomed to pay for implements. As a result of crop conditions and the outbreak of war in Europe, the land boom in western Canada collapsed. The great Rumely tractor and thresher consolidation effected in 1912 failed, and Harvester experienced the most unfortunate credit ratio in its history. The Company had exceeded all others in sales volume because of its great distributing ability; but its position was nevertheless not a dominating one. That was to come with the small tractor which could be built in quantities by production methods and which, consistent with Harvester traditions, could be a machine for all farmers. An industry may render service best when it deals with the many, not with the few.

The credit for producing the first light tractor must be given to the Bull Tractor Company, which in 1913 introduced a remarkable and radically different machine. The tractor weighed only three thousand pounds. It was provided with a single huge bull wheel and a direct connected two-cylinder engine without transmission gears or differential. It sold for the unbelievably low price of $395. The little Bull gave place next year to the Big Bull, a slightly more powerful machine. It was never a mechanically sound product, but its commercial popularity was such that it swept the field.

International Harvester was quick to follow this opportunity. It introduced a kerosene-burning, slow-speed, single-cylinder machine with planetary transmission and a single drive chain, known as the Mogul 8–16 (meaning eight horse-power at the drawbar and sixteen at the belt pulley), which was built at Tractor Works. Then, because of the fact that there were two lines of dealers to foster, another tractor was developed at Milwaukee, the Titan 10–20. This was a two-cylinder affair with high-tension ignition, a standard type of transmission, and a double chain drive. It had been intended to accompany the Deering line, just as the Mogul was classified with the McCormick; but this plan of alleviations would not work. The same men had designed both machines, and quite naturally they built into the second the experience gained in making the first. Furthermore, the Mogul would pull two plow bottoms under average conditions, whereas the more powerful Titan would handle three.

The Company was still making large tractors both at Milwaukee and at Tractor Works; but the vitality of the industry lay in the smaller machines. In 1915, the financial situation of farmers began to improve, and, spurred by the prospect of war prices, they planned to bring more extensive acreage into production. So strong was their interest in labor-saving, cost-reducing equipment that manufacturers and salesmen began to engage in a mad scramble to enter the tractor business. A man with any new idea would build a tractor around it and rush out to the country to look for purchasers. There were one hundred and thirty listed tractor companies, whereas but fifty were actually able to make deliveries.

The Winnipeg contest had given place to one at Fremont, Nebraska. With the great spread of tractor interest, it became necessary in 1916 to organize a circuit of large demonstrations. Numberless local shows also took place in connection with county fairs or to settle competitive controversies. The national demonstrations were held in sequence at Dallas, Hutchinson, St. Louis, Fremont, Cedar Rapids, Bloomington, Indianapolis, and Madison. Tractor farming was becoming the order of the day. Nearly all the machines manufactured in 1916 were sold in the United States. The war-time demand was especially keen in 1917, when, out of a total of over sixty-two thousand made, fifteen thousand were shipped abroad. England, France, and Italy bought most of them to aid their food production.

In 1918, tractor production more than doubled. There were over two hundred tractor companies competing for the rapidly growing business. Bull dropped out of the picture, and Holt was making treads for tanks. Most of the manufacturers were transient companies which fell quickly or never got started. Many of the pioneers of the tractor industry had collapsed with the decline of the big tractor and more of the weaker newcomers were passing out each year. Nevertheless, the insatiable war-time demands for food production and the soaring prices of farm products made the problem of tractor manufacture seem easy. International Harvester was the leading producer, followed by Case, Avery, and Moline.

Henry Ford's intention to build farm tractors was announced in 1915, and, though he probably never said it, he was credited with the intention of selling his proposed machine for two hundred dollars. The miracles he had accomplished with his car made the public believe that, when it appeared, it would be the last word, and that a 'jitney tractor' would bring salvation to agriculture. He had been conducting experimental work for a long time on his own estates and began production in 1917 with the sale of six thousand to the British Government. Ford tractors first appeared on American farms in 1918.

The Ford tractor — or Fordson, as it was properly called — was the first of the unit types to achieve widespread popularity. Its comparatively low price soon gave it the leading position in the industry and its construction helped to set the type for all tractors of that day. There can be no question that the development of tractor design had been to a certain extent haphazard. For years it had been entirely in the hands of implement men who had too slight a contact with the refinements and research of the automobile industry. Because it is so purely a farm machine, it was eminently correct for the tractor to remain an inherent part of the implement business; and therefore it can be understood why, before 1917, it partook so little of automobile standards. The first machines had depended upon their bulk of material to give them strength. Even the intermediate tractors, like the Mogul and the Titan, were excessively heavy, weighing two hundred pounds for each engine horsepower as compared to one hundred and fifty-six pounds for the tractor of 1931. With them began the inclusion of modern features, such as high duty bearings and alloy steels, but they did not in any intimate way resemble the precision engineered and manufactured masterpiece of to-day.

Also in 1917, the Society of Tractor Engineers amalgamated with the Society of Automotive Engineers. Immediately the tractor companies gained the benefit of the experience-earned knowledge of the automobile world. This the tractor men needed badly. There were many things they did not know about the fine points of internal combustion, gears, and the like; much that they had to learn about heat treatment of steel and the strength of materials. Standardization of parts, also, although widely practiced in the case of agricultural implements, had made but slight progress in tractors. Such refinement of design as made the Ford tractor noteworthy had been too much a closed book.

Looking ahead from that time or back from this, I can realize how much the International Harvester Company had to learn; and I can take pride in the speed with which we acquired and assimilated the necessary knowledge. That we were able to do so was our salvation. The Mogul 8–16 had given way to a four-cylinder tractor of the same power; but the good old Titan 10–20 still forged on, most popular of all tractors, and the men of Milwaukee Works were accustomed to relate proudly how one was started every four-and-a-half minutes. Even in 1919, tractors were the largest single item of our production. We knew how much money they were saving farmers, we knew what service they were performing. And we knew that the story of farm power, begun when the reaper took the place of a scytheman's muscles, was being retold in the tractor.

CHAPTER X

LAWSUITS, WAR, AND DEPRESSION

SHORTLY after the formation of the International Harvester Company was announced in 1902, certain individuals raised the cry that here was another private corporation formed to mulct the public. The early years of the twentieth century were a period when many believed that consolidation was intended to enrich a few business barons at the expense of the many. Politicians all over the country began to inveigh against the 'trusts,' political campaigns turned on the question, people became aroused at what they feared would be an invasion of personal well-being by private capital. It is therefore probable that, whether it deserved it or not, rural opinion would have been skeptical of the new corporation.

The early skepticism was temporarily fanned into active opposition by petty politicians, eager to ride to higher offices on such public clamor as they could arouse. It is pleasant to know that long since, after the hue and cry has been faced and has subsided and, out of closer acquaintance with the Company, farmers have learned to regard it with respect and esteem. They have discovered the benefit to them of Harvester's business methods, and they have come to appreciate the quality of its machines and its services. They have heard charges made, they have seen lawsuits filed, the stated object of which was to protect the farm from the grasp of the 'harvester trust' — and now they know that the tribunals of the public have vindicated the Company from every charge of wrongful practice. Rural opinion is no longer skeptical: it is positive, hearty, friendly in a man-to-man sort of way. Out of their own experience farmers have welcomed the International Harvester Company to the farm side of the farm problem.

But in 1905, officials in certain States began to attack the Company. Their cry was that the agricultural implement 'trust' enjoyed a monopoly because of valuable patent rights; that prior to 1902, the trade was in a normal, healthy condition, and that the only possible object of consolidation was more easily to crush competitors and gouge consumers; that prices and profits had been materially increased; that the products of the new company were sold cheaper abroad than at home, thus making the American farmer pay the price of volume production; and that individual representatives had committed every crime in the penal code of commerce.

As is known to-day, this local agitation was the result of the acts of other consolidations, or the refusal of the Harvester Company to submit to public or private extortion, or the endeavor of self-seeking minor officials to get preferment out of what they thought would be a popular clamor, or it arose simply out of the 'trust-busting' temper of the times. I presume that I myself, who am so obviously partisan and who know so intimately the high ideals inherited by my father and his associates from my grandfather, am not equipped to speak impartially on these matters. I also know we salesmen were invariably cautioned to live our business lives by the same high dictates of personal conscience which guided the owners of the business and our other superior officers. And I am very well aware how, now that legal difficulties are happily a thing of the past and the Company has been vindicated, these ideals have permeated every rank of the many associated activities. They have inspired all Harvester men to a business life hewn four-square with the best rules of ethical conduct. I venture to state that if a Harvester man now chose to commit an economic crime, the sin would expose itself.

Whether or not I may qualify sufficiently as an historian to speak impersonally of these matters, let me say this in comment on the charges: They are all of them false. No one of them has ever been proved in or out of court. All of them have been disproved to the complete satisfaction of every court or other tribunal that has ever considered them. One and all have been withdrawn, jointly or severally, by every State or Federal prosecutor who has ever attacked the Company. In all its history the sole fault found with the Company has been its size resulting from consolidation, not its conduct. Because of this, it has paid the penalty of years of litigation. But if institutions, like people, may be judged by their acts, it can be proud of the fact that no competitor, few retail dealers, and scant farmers have ever testified against it.

The selling branch of the Harvester Company was fined in Arkansas in 1906 because of the size of its capital and withdrew from the State until 1913 when the hostile law was repealed at the request of the entire agricultural and business community. Ouster proceedings were brought in Kansas in 1906 and settled in 1910. Many farmers testified that prices had not been increased and that service had been improved. The State Supreme Court therefore assessed a fine on purely legal grounds and permitted the business to continue, holding that it was not in the public interest to eject the Company. In 1907, an ouster suit was brought in Missouri which resulted in the complete exoneration of the Company as to everything except the legality of its formation through consolidation, a suspended sentence on that sole ground, and this flattering statement by Missouri's Chief Justice: 'It would be an injury to the people of this State to forbid the International Harvester Company to do business here.' In 1907, the Company evacuated Texas to protect its employees who would have been liable to personal fines if they sold its commodities within that State, and thereafter a judgment of ouster was entered. When I was a branch manager in Kansas and Oklahoma, I used to stand by the border of forbidden Texas and long to explore it, but we were under the strictest orders not to go. But in 1919, after the decree of ouster had been modified to permit it to return, the Harvester Company came back to the State by invitation of the people. In Kentucky, where eighty-eight per cent of all fines collected went as fees to public officials, the Company fled from a horde of petty county suits and remained away until the State anti-trust laws were declared unconstitutional.

After the period of local attacks, Harvester was called upon to face the hostility of the United States Government, which was a far more serious matter. The first of the two Federal suits, which shadowed the middle period of the Company's history, was brought in 1912 as a partial result of an investigation by the United States Bureau of Corporations. The Government's petition charged that the Company had been formed to effect a competition-destroying monopoly in harvesting machinery and binder twine. It claimed that over eighty-five per cent of all harvesting equipment sold in the United States were International products; that prices had been advanced to the grave injury of the farmer; and that the Company had striven successfully to eliminate competition. This had been accomplished, it was alleged, by exclusive contracts with local dealers, by threats to dealers, and by gobbling up all available dealers. A huge patent monopoly had been created, it was averred, thus preventing others from entering the harvester field. It was charged that competitors had been purchased and absorbed and their products abandoned once they were out of the way, that potential competitors were frightened off, and that unfair trade practices were resorted to in order to injure existing competitors.

These charges were unjust and untrue. They hurt both the Company's business and its ability to serve the farmer. Self-seeking politicians cheered and farmers wondered how an institution they were learning to respect could be so sinful. Harvester men, who knew the Company's policy because they were its living expression, bitterly resented the accusations. It became their turn to applaud when testimony in the case was taken. The Government could find in the entire country but a corporal's guard of witnesses to come forward and testify against the Company. Several of the harshest allegations were abandoned when the case came to trial. All of them — just as in the earlier State ouster suits — except the charge of a preponderant percentage in the old harvester lines, fell to the ground for want of even the slightest shred of proof.

It would be tedious to follow the case through the story of the testimony of twelve hundred witnesses which filled ten thousand printed pages. Suffice it to say that Judges Smith and Hook, of the United States District Court of Minnesota, gave the Company a clean bill of health for its conduct, but convicted it because of its origin through the consolidation of former competitors. Judge Sanborn dissented, holding that the absence of injury to the public and the freedom of competition that had been proved should govern the issue.

The adverse decision of the Court was not based on

the ground that the organizers of the Company had an unlawful purpose, or that competition was not free and active, or that the Company's business conduct had been wrongful. On the contrary, Harvester's methods were characterized as 'honorable, clean, and fair,' and the many charges of improper business practices made in the Government petition were called unwarranted and without foundation. The legal issue, as it lay in the minds of the majority of the Court, was this: The consolidation of the five companies in 1902 had quite naturally eliminated competition between them. Trade in binders, mowers, and rakes was held to be directly restrained by the fact that International thus acquired such a substantial percentage of the total business. This restraint was held to create a potential monopoly in violation of the Sherman Law, not because of the Company's actual conduct, but because of its alleged power to dominate — a power which probably did not exist and certainly had not been exercised. The Court therefore ordered the Company dissolved into such separate parts as would be necessary to restore competition.

It is hard to believe that the mild-tempered president of the International Harvester Company, whose great sense of honor and justice and fair play had set the pattern for his organization's conduct, was not disgusted when he said: 'The conclusion arrived at seems to be that the Harvester is a good but illegal trust. Its business has been conducted fairly and the economies secured by its organization have inured to the benefit of its customers, the farmers, but nevertheless its existence is illegal.'

The opinion of the Court was filed in August, 1914. The International Harvester Company immediately appealed to the United States Supreme Court. There, because of the importance of the legal issues involved, it was set at the head of the docket and was argued in April, 1915. The Justices could not agree, so they ordered a rehearing. A year and a half dragged along, with no adjudication of the Government's interpretation of the Sherman Law and no relief for the Company from the threat of dissolution. Early in 1917, it was thought by both sides that the Harvester case could be heard simultaneously with the case of the United States Steel Corporation, both of which turned on the question whether a combination which occupied a 'preponderant position' in its business constituted a violation of the law. Again the case was argued and again the Supreme Court failed to reach an agreement. The situation was getting desperate.

In the meantime the United States had entered the World War. Seven important anti-trust suits, including the Harvester and Steel cases, were awaiting judicial settlement. If the Government should win, seven important sources of munitions and supplies essential to the country and to the war might be crippled, and any new financing required by a dissolution decree would draw funds away from the Nation's war chest. So, early in 1918, they were all postponed. Further delay was more than the long-suffering International Harvester Company could stand, and in the following summer it accepted terms of honorable surrender. Any definite situation was to be preferred to the uncertainty of never-ending litigation.

Formed in 1902 with no wrongful purpose and in the belief that it was entirely legal, the Company had from 1905 been the object of attack in various State courts. Its conduct had invariably been found blameless. The Federal suit was brought in 1912, and six years later it was still undecided. If the Government should win, the Company would be dismembered in 1918 or some later year on the strength of testimony taken in 1913 for legal errors committed in 1902. In the meantime the war had played havoc with its entire affairs. For business reasons, the foreign factories and sales as well as the bulk of the new lines had been segregated in a separate company, the International Harvester Corporation. But, because of war losses, the Corporation could not find capital, for example for needed tractor expansion; and if the original company were dissolved, it could give the Corporation no financial assistance. Therefore, it was obviously necessary to put the two halves of the business together again, provided an understanding with the Government could be reached. Any even partly satisfactory compromise would be better than continued nerve-racking uncertainty.

A so-called consent decree of 1918, which was later approved by the Court, was arranged between the Harvester lawyers, John P. Wilson, Edgar A. Bancroft, and William D. McHugh, who had so ably led the Company's long fight, and the Attorney-General. The appeal to the Supreme Court was dismissed, which in effect sustained the Government's view of the legal issue. The International agreed to divest itself of the Osborne, Champion, and Milwaukee lines of harvesting machines and the works where they were made. Beginning with 1920, it was to have no more than one dealer in a town. At the end of eighteen months after the close of the war, the Government was to have the right to reopen the case to determine whether these measures had resulted in the restoration of competition. As a by-product of this compromise, Harvester was to be permitted to take on the manufacture and sale of plows — which was only fair, since it could not hope to sell the three harvester lines except to some plow group. But under this decree a considerable volume of sales and the goodwill of three established trade names would be transferred away from the International to competitors, who would thereby grow stronger. Also, whatever it might gain from entry into the already occupied plow field would hardly compensate for the loss of five thousand organized and effective retail selling agencies with which business to the amount of $17,000,000 a year was then being done. Cyrus H. McCormick doubtless felt as dispirited as did his father when he was denied the extension of his patents or was beaten by Manny.

If the very natural desire to be free from the Damoclean threat of the Government suit was not an amply sufficient reason for the Harvester Company's agreement to the so-called consent decree, it may also be understood that at the same time the war was presenting an apparently insuperable obstacle to progress. But, however difficult had been the years since 1914, the outbreak of the war furnished the best possible tribute to the basic nature of the Company's activities and to the world-wide need for its services. The armies might fight, but they and the civilian population behind them had to eat. Men were with the colors, and, as in the case of the American Civil War, machines alone could take their places on the farms of the embattled nations. Quite naturally the war restricted the Harvester Company's former European volume; but farms demanded equipment, and, with the exception of a few small implement factories in France, Bohemia, Sweden, and England, there were practically no European manufacturers of harvesting and other agricultural machinery. The world trade was virtually in the hands of Americans and Canadians. The International Harvester Company was the largest factor, with Massey-Harris of Toronto second. When women took the place of men on the farms of France, Germany, and Britain, and when great estates, hitherto devoted to other purposes, were turned to grain production, Harvester's machines were required in great numbers. Its binders and mowers were rushed to take the place of the still-used scythe, its tractors were pressed into service in the stead of farm horses become army mounts. Under the compulsion of war necessity, Europe learned, as had America, that farm production costs could be reduced by the use of modern equipment.

The foreign factories, if they were able to operate at all, were quite naturally hampered by the difficulty of securing adequate materials. The German twine mill had to close because of inability to secure a supply of fiber, and the French factory was being used as a cavalry barracks by the Germans. As soon as the United States entered the war, the German factory passed out of the Company's control and into the hands of a government receiver. But prices of farm products were rising in the face of the unusual demand for food, and the volume of sales remained fairly steady. The various governments, of course, controlled purchases and restricted them to necessities; so it can be said that International Harvester implements and tractors served the cause of food production as ably as had McCormick reapers in Civil War times.

As the war dragged along, it became apparent that decline of business would not be the only loss the Company would have to face. Because of the non-existence of exchange, it had been impossible to transfer funds from parts of Europe to America. All trade with Germany was embargoed; Russia was living behind a wall of war. The Russian factory continued to operate during 1917; but when the Russian political, economic, and social structure collapsed, it became known that the losses in central and eastern Europe would be calamitous.

When the picture of this disaster became complete after the war, the Company had to face the fact that every penny it had ever invested in Russia had gone. All of the profits of the Russian business up to 1914 had been put back into the many branch warehouses and the factory; and after the commencement of the war the great stocks of machines and materials on hand had been converted. The proceeds were on deposit in various banks, the value of which paper, after the Bolshevik rebellion, declined to nothing. The factory itself remained in the hands of Harvester representatives until 1924, when the Soviet Government simply walked in and took it over, without payment or promise of one cent of compensation. It did this because the Company was obviously unwilling to sink additional money in Russia and continued to operate the plant only so long as materials could be purchased from the proceeds of the constantly decreasing Russian business itself. Russia needed machines, but the total collapse of the nation's structure made the hoe rather than the *lobogreika* the necessary measure of farm equipment. Factory, warehouses, inventories, and bank deposits — everything Harvester had in Russia vanished. Such satisfaction as the Company could find in the fact that, due to the faith of the workmen, the plant remained in its possession long after every other foreign property had been nationalized, was the sole compensation for twenty years of service to Russian agriculture. There were losses, too, in Germany, Austria, and Roumania. The French factory had been stripped of every bit of equipment. The sum of the cost of the war was staggering. The International Harvester Company remained solvent only because of wise management, a widely diversified world business, and an aggressively conservative financial system.

The effect of the war in America was measured by the frantic war-born industrial boom. The Company's war record, though perhaps praiseworthy, was not essentially different from that of many other great American commercial institutions. Its subscriptions to loans and its donations to war charities were large; many of its employees enlisted in the army or the navy, and too many fell in defense of the country; and at one time or another four of the seven chief operating officials were in Government service in Washington. It also made enormous numbers of shell-adapters, hand grenades, motor-truck bodies, transport wagons, and artillery wheels; but its best service of supply was to produce its own essential machines.

It can be easily remembered how the war-time demand for labor, food, and every type of supply sent the cost of all production skyrocketing. Where conservative business men would have much preferred a stable market, the price of every article of consumption increased. Steel, pig iron, and lumber advanced; and wages more than doubled. Then men discovered that each one of them was not only an employee whose pay envelope was thicker, but also a consumer of other people's products, and that price was, after all, merely a reflection of cost. Thus the High Cost of Living came to be a subject of general discussion, too many people in all walks of life sought to counteract this new and mysterious doctrine by getting more in income than they gave in efficiency, the evil of 'cost plus' war production sapped the morals of management and labor alike, and the war stalked into history, as sorry a thing for civilians as for the men at the front.

By the beginning of 1919, when every one was expecting war prosperity to crash, the cost of living had increased seventy per cent as compared with 1914, the wages of Harvester workers had doubled, purchased materials had kept pace, and the price of its machines had advanced by a half. The prices of most articles used by American manufacturers, as for example steel and coal, were stabilized under Government control; and farm products, as for example wheat, were similarly regulated. But America paid dearly for what it had to buy from abroad. Nitrates made Chile rich, and a sisal fiber monopoly in Yucatan took millions from the American user of binder twine. Fiber rose to the hitherto undreamed-of height of nineteen cents per pound, but Mexico lay beyond the reach of the arm of the Sherman Law. Then, because the fattened prosperity of war days did not seem to vanish easily, all classes of men went economically mad. Possessions were discarded in favor of new purchases, labor demanded and secured an increasing portion of the consumer's dollar, prices soared beyond the artificially high levels of the war, and quick riches for all took the place of efficiency as a living ideal. By the end of 1920, when the specter of reckoning stalked upon the scene, wages throughout the country were two-and-a-half times the rate of 1914, and the weighted cost of living, which reflected the higher price of everything one had to buy, had doubled.

It is true of the agricultural implement business that, although its peaks and valleys roughly follow general business, both depression and recovery reach it later than the rest of commerce and industry. Depression moves from the East to the West: scattered farmers of the country feel trends and tendencies less quickly than do the organized inhabitants of an urban community. But hindsight is always better informed than foresight, and it is probable that these economic axioms were not appreciated in 1921. At all events, every business unit which did not immediately feel a cessation of buying power and recognize depression believed that, by the operation of some special providence, its own sales would continue unabated. This error of judgment seriously affected the whole of American industry.

The stronger implement companies, such as Deere, Oliver, Massey-Harris, Case, and Harvester, had realized that the frantic prosperity of those days was not real. They did not know when the break would come, but some of them had had foresight enough to create special reserves to provide for the sure losses of an indeterminate future. They were able to pull through while some weaker companies were wiped out; and they did so in spite of the fact that the depression years following 1920 were more disastrous than the damage occasioned by the war.

The measure of that business disaster, when the International Harvester Company rocked and bowed before the storm that wrecked so many enterprises, is quickly told. Wages were twice reduced; the salary of every executive, high and low, was cut; expenditures for improvements, shut off for a time during the war, were again restricted; and all the factories were closed or operated on pitiably reduced schedules. The 1921 business amounted to but half of the previous year's volume. Large losses were sustained in the domestic trade, the only profit earned was made abroad, and reduced dividends were paid out of surplus. In 1922, the situation was slightly better — or perhaps it would be more accurate to say that Harvester men had become somewhat more accustomed to their misfortune. The price of every article sold by the Company had, of course, been slashed to the bone, but buying did not revive. The year's net profits again failed by several million dollars to provide even the reduced dividends.

It must not be thought that this was an isolated tragedy. The whole economic mechanism of American life was crippled; and the business of farming — together with everything dependent upon it — suffered most of all. The price of wheat, which in the halcyon days of the war had been 'kept down' to three dollars a bushel, fell in 1921 to a dollar. Cotton dropped twenty cents a pound. Corn remained unharvested in the fields or was burned for fuel. The price of cattle and hogs fell until every animal was a liability. Worst of all, the farmers had, in effect, been speculating as wildly in land as urbanites had been in the swollen profits of industry. Land values collapsed all over the country, and many a hard-working purchaser of inflated acres was immediately bankrupt. The country banks had lent money to finance the acquisition, for double and treble prices, of fields which could not possibly be made to pay, now that the days of high prices for farm products were over. They could foreclose on their mortgages, but that would avail them nothing. Frozen credits became the order of the day in the country as in the city. The farmer could not make a profit on what he had to sell, his usual channels of credit were closed, he had nothing wherewith to buy. All he could do was hope — and go on working.

The enormous damage caused by the depression can be appreciated when it is remembered that, before the end of 1920, the International Harvester Company had provided an inventory of materials for a 1921 business which was expected to be huge. The inflated value of this inventory was due to the highest cost of materials in all the Company's history. Then the decline began. Almost overnight steel, for example, fell from a high point of the year of seventy-five dollars per ton to thirty dollars. Machines made of high-priced material had to be sold for depreciated values. Therefore, the Company had not only to bear the brunt of the shrinkage of its own inventory value, but was compelled either to sustain those of its dealers who had stocked up with machines in anticipation of bumper business or to see them collapse. It withstood the shock by the same means that had aided it through the calamity of war losses.

Without any question wise management had much to do with the fact that International Harvester succeeded in weathering the storm. Since late 1918, Cyrus H. McCormick had been chairman of the board, and, although no longer directly concerned with the details of operations, his kindly and wise influence was strong. His brother Harold, a product of the same tradition, was president for a time and Alex Legge was general manager — Legge, the same forceful leader of other days, but with his experience deepened and his outlook broadened by contact with the many leaders the war brought to Washington. The various operating departmental heads were largely the same men as those who had given Harvester Spirit to the organization. Now, however, their duty was to rein in instead of to push on toward the triumphs of an expanding business. They used the tragic lessons of the period of depression to make the Company efficient.

No amount of efficiency alone, however, could have saved money enough out of operating economies to permit Harvester to live on. Huge losses were written off both in 1921 and 1922 to cover inventory depreciation. The Harvester management had known that the agricultural implement industry must be as prepared for valleys as for peaks, and that the abnormal prosperity of post-war days could not last forever. It did not foresee the imminence of the crash, but it had planned against ultimate depression by storing up a buffer of accumulated reserves. As the price of materials and labor increased, beginning in 1917, a suitable portion of the earnings was segregated against inevitable reaction by carrying the basic inventory at 1916 costs. This advance provision of a cushion to soften the blow of an unseen storm was badly needed; for during the two years of business depression, the Company consumed all the reserves, made virtually no profit, and met such reduced dividends as it paid out of surplus. When, by the end of 1922, costs of materials had settled down to a new and saner level, the price of incipient disaster had been met out of inventory write-downs and reduced surplus. Parenthetically it is pleasant to record the fact that the cushion policy of advance provision for an unexpected business decline is being continued through the medium of reserves.

By 1923, the low prices for farm products recovered somewhat, the farmer began to buy again, and International's business began slowly to recover. But in July of that year, the skies again darkened as the Attorney-General of the United States filed a petition to reopen the old anti-trust suit and the settlement of 1918. This time the Government's concern was more for Harvester's competitors than for the farmer. The main allegation was that the 1918 consent decree had failed to reëstablish competition and that the Harvester Company was selling at cost with a view of eliminating competitors. It was said that the sale of the Champion, Osborne, and Milwaukee lines had achieved merely an immaterial effect, and that their purchasers and other competitors were growing weaker each year under the strokes of International policy. Where the original suit had sought to prove injury to the farmer through overpricing and other alleged nefarious acts (all of which were disproved), the second suit suggested that competitors were being harmed by underpricing.

The St. Paul District Court, however, found otherwise. In May, 1925, two of the three judges decided for the Company. They found that trade was free and not restrained or monopolized, that the Harvester Company's portion of the country's harvesting machinery trade had declined, and that prices were low and favorable to the farmer. One judge held that because of its size the Company had the power to do evil, and should therefore be restrained. This time it was the Government, the loser in the case, that appealed to the Supreme Court.

There, in 1927, it pleaded that competition similar to what had existed before 1902 should be reëstablished; but this contention the Court refused to sustain. It expressed the opinion that the Harvester Company had complied with the 1918 decision in good faith and should not be dismembered. Much of the evidence had been founded on a 1920 report of the Federal Trade Commission which, on the basis of *ex parte* evidence taken in advance of the test period provided by the Court's decision, had expressed the belief that the consent decree would prove a failure. This report the Supreme Court brushed aside, as it did all of the Government's argument. The growth of the Company was due to the development of the full line, not to the disputed harvesting machinery. The sale of the three lines to responsible manufacturers had been made as required by the 1918 decree. The limitation to but one dealer in a community had been adhered to and had been of substantial assistance to competitors, as they themselves had testified. Harvester had not used its strength oppressively, it had not sought to dominate the trade, it had not employed unfair practices against competitors. 'The law,' said the Supreme Court, 'does not make the mere size of a corporation ... an offense when unaccompanied by unlawful conduct in the exercise of its power.'

The opinion went on to point out that in 1923 the International had as many and stronger harvesting-machine competitors than in 1911; that its percentage of the trade had declined; and that the entry of new competitors into the field proved the freedom of competitive conditions.

Thus at last, after so many years of doubt, the International Harvester Company was free. The case had dragged along for such a time that harvesting machines, for which the Government was fighting, were no longer a major consideration in the industry. The very charge had veered from high prices and injury to consumers to low prices and injury to competitors. Three of the nine Justices of the Court had through the years become disqualified by participation in or contact with the early stages of the case. The Company, organized in 1902 and pilloried from 1905 to 1927, was at last returned to ordinary life and to the judgment of ordinary rules of conduct where an individual may be valued, not by a nonexistent reputation, but by his acts.

I shall never forget the scene in the Harvester offices as word of the Supreme Court's decision, read with due preliminary formality and distressing deliberation, kept coming over the long-distance telephone. I suppose we might have preserved a philosophic calm — but we could not. With the words, 'We cannot sustain this contention...' we knew that we had won. We had known that we were right — but were we within the law?

We had the tradition of an ideal of service behind us; the fruition of our hopes lay ahead. Perhaps we had been attending too much to our business and had taken too little time for the theories underlying academic debate, perhaps we lived too close to the actuality of existence to have sufficient concern for the maze of the law. We could not understand why, if our acts measured four-square with every standard of business conduct, we should be drawn and quartered for the legal errors of 1902. Now we knew we were lawful as well as right and could continue our work. Again that subtle influence called Harvester Spirit, working quietly and grandly and justly in our lives and in the deeds which were the constructive reaction of our efforts, had rescued the Company from the supposed hostility of the alleged law.

Of all the baseless charges leveled at the Harvester Company throughout the years, there is one other which deserves to be dignified by more than passing mention, and that, not because it has ever had any foundation, but because of its persistence. Soon after the formation of the International, the story was somehow started that it was discriminating against American farmers and favoring foreign farmers by selling its American-made implements cheaper abroad than at home. Never the subject of litigation, no one proved the charge or attempted to prove it; but politicians did not hesitate to repeat it whenever it served their interests to bait the Harvester Company. It persists strangely to this day, notwithstanding the fact that not a single instance of dumping Harvester goods abroad has ever been found.

No better illustration could be discovered of the difficulty of truth overtaking falsehood. Harvester Company officials have denied the allegation whenever they could confront it. It was investigated in 1912 by direction of Secretary Nagel, of the Department of Commerce and Labor, and found to be untrue. It was investigated again in 1928 by the United States Consular Service at the instance of Secretary of Commerce Herbert Hoover, and again found to be untrue. The facts have been publicly referred to as conclusive by Secretary of Agriculture Hyde and by members of Congress. They are posted on the record where those who run may read — and yet the twenty-five-year-old falsehood may be long in dying. The Company has never sold goods abroad at less profit than at home. Its foreign prices are based on the domestic price with proper adjustment to cover the cost of export packing, freight, foreign duties, and difference in selling expense. The foreign farmer thus necessarily pays a higher price than the farmer at home; but the Company's price structure is fair to both. Farmers all over the world, the American farmer most of all, have gained the benefit of mass production in American factories.

American business men are honest, by and large; and American industry is true. Its captains are not prone to build themselves marble mausoleums nor can they take their gains with them into another world. But they can bequeath their responsibilities to successors whom they have trained to carry on their work to greater heights. Thus they may live, and thus they may be known by their fruits.

CHAPTER XI

RECOVERY AND RECONSTRUCTION

THE several years succeeding 1918 were, in the main, a period of recovery and reconstruction for the International Harvester Company. It had weathered legal storms in several States and then found itself really popular with its customers. Farm opinion had been won, partly by Harvester's honorable business conduct, mostly by a growing recognition of the service which, in an ever more definite way, it was performing for agriculture. The period from 1914 to, say, 1922 should have been one of better business rising on the foundation of the Company's first ten years. But the Great War brought losses, the period of depression was fraught with misfortune, and compliance with the 1918 decree added many serious problems. Actually, these years were a period when hope alternated with dashed expectations and then new plans.

It will be remembered that the Company was compelled by the terms of the 1918 consent decree to sell the Champion, Osborne, and Milwaukee lines of harvesting machinery. The first two were immediately sold, Osborne to the Emerson-Brantingham Company, of Rockford (present-day successor of Manny, who fought such stiff legal battles against the original Cyrus Hall McCormick), and Champion to B. F. Avery, of Louisville. The former enjoyed a nation-wide plow and tillage business and, in the heyday of the big tractor, had enjoyed a successful threshing-machine trade. The other had an entirely worth-while reputation in the South, and to a certain extent in the Northwest as well, for its plows, cultivators, and other small implements. Both felt their positions would be strengthened by the addition of a developed, established harvesting-machine line, and both promised to be strong competitors.

Neither, however, wished to buy the Osborne or Champion factories which the original decree required Harvester to sell, as both already possessed ample manufacturing capacity. So, with the consent of the Government, the Court permitted International to continue to operate the two plants for other purposes. Champion Works was renamed Springfield and converted to motor-truck production, and in its new guise came ultimately to enjoy a prosperity it had never known before. A portion of the Osborne establishment, now called Auburn Works, was retained for its traditional cultivator and tillage production. In 1924, the Milwaukee line was sold to Moline, a name famous throughout the world for plows. Both Emerson-Brantingham and Moline had been in a strong financial and trade position, but they were sadly hurt by the depression of 1921, and, while both worked along for quite a while, both have recently sold out to stronger companies.

The single-dealer requirement was at first regarded by the Company's management as nothing short of a calamity. Many thousand dealers had to be abandoned. Many were long-standing associates whose experience began in the old harvester days long before the consolidation. The choice between two friends is usually an impossible dilemma and such separation is too frequently the cause of enmity. It was believed that many of the dealers cut off to comply with the decree would either provide the severest competition or would knife the Company for having cast them away. Old McCormick and Deering dealers by the hundreds were eliminated; yet, though they could not have liked the situation, most of them understood that the dictates of the law and not the wishes of the Company were responsible. Where Harvester had 21,800 dealers in 1917, but 13,860 of these remained in 1919. Competitors testified in the second Government suit that this narrowing of the International sales outlet aided their own search for dealers and thus increased their ability to compete for harvesting-machine sales.

This was undoubtedly so, since no product, however excellent, is merchantable unless it can be placed aggressively before the public. Harvester's own previous channels of distribution were partially dammed and its sales effort was crippled. The Company was placed in a situation that affected none of its competitors, for they could, if they wished, seek business relations with its dealers while it was prohibited from contact with theirs. While this fact undoubtedly caused Harvester salesmen to pursue every possible opportunity for trade more keenly, it is also certain that it has been the cause of a smaller volume of business than would otherwise have been secured. But for the single-dealer limitation of the Court's decree, Harvester's volume would be larger than it now is.

Nevertheless, as the years passed after 1918, it began to be apparent that the provision of the Court's decree limiting the Company to a single dealer in each community would not prove to be so great a hindrance to Harvester's future as had been feared. The double McCormick and Deering lines of implements could not be maintained in the United States with but one agent in a community. Therefore, a composite type of grain binder containing what were thought to be the best points of the two old machines, called the McCormick-Deering, was designed and introduced to the trade in 1923. The new binder was immediately followed with other implements which were either planned anew from the combined advantages of the two lines or were selected bodily from the old name groups as representing the best of the art; and thus the present McCormick-Deering line came into being. It, of course, included all types of farm operating equipment, especially the various tractor models. The salesmen liked it because it was complete and allowed them to center their effort on one instead of a double line.

The advantage to farmers and to dealers of such a procedure is easily apparent. Service was facilitated. Each International dealer all over the length and breadth of the land was able to stock, sell, and service all the tractors, motor trucks, grain binders, harvester-threshers, corn tools, and the many other items of the McCormick-Deering line. Finally, and of possibly greater importance for the future, the experimental effort required to work out improvements was made easier and could be keener. A man works best when he has undivided confidence in the single task at hand.

An almost equally definitive result of the 1918 decree was the addition of plows to the Company's business. This matter had long been in the minds of the salesmen, who had for years seen Deere, the original full-line company, expanding into the harvesting-machine field. Naturally they wished to take on plows. Therefore in 1919, after a survey of existing organizations, International Harvester bought the Parlin and Orendorff Company, third in size of the important plow factors in the country. It will be remembered how the original Parlin came to Canton, Illinois, in 1840, and how his business, growing rapidly under the forward thrust of his energy, was given a further impulse by the genius for sales of his partner, Orendorff. P & O, as the two men called their company, soon added walking cultivators to its line, the first corn lister, a sulky plow, and finally the gang plow. Its large heavy engine gang of 1894 has been called one of the first tractor plows. It made corn planters and certain beet tools. Neither the first partners nor their sons who succeeded them interested themselves at all in such production methods as standardization or the elimination of variety; for it is said that at the time of the purchase by Harvester they were making over fourteen hundred sizes and kinds of implements.

With the addition of plows and other correlated implements, the International Harvester Company was for the first time able to offer a complete line of machines to the trade. Its full line, begun so soon after the formation of the Company, was at last developed — at least within the scope of existing knowledge. This account of the invention of the reaper and what came out of it is not a book of machinery; and yet it may be instructive to follow the cycle of a farmer's year and see what part in it the machine descendants of the reaper can play.

If the farmer's lot is cast in the wheat belt, he can, if he so desires, perform his every operation with Harvester equipment. He can plow his land with whatever type of instrument suits the condition of his soil, harrow it in any known way, and pack his seed-bed to conserve the subsurface moisture. He can drill his seed in close rows or wide ones, and, if he be so minded, can cover a narrow strip or one thirty feet wide. When his crop has ripened, he can harvest it with a reaper or a horse-drawn binder or with a wide header-harvester or a header-binder. Or he can gather his crop with a combined harvester-thresher prepared to deliver wheat in sacks or spout it into a tank. If his farm lies in a moist district where the grain is too wet at the time of harvest for threshing, and he can still justify a large amount of fast work, he can use a tractor binder. Twine to tie his sheaves is Harvester-made and so is his stationary threshing machine.

A corn-belt farmer can plow his land with implements designed for row-crop agriculture. Then he can plant his corn and cultivate it with whatever implement suits his fancy or the fashion of his neighborhood. When harvest time comes, he can bind it vertically or horizontally according to the length of the stalk; or he can snap and husk the ears and shred the stalks, or pick the ears from the standing corn, and husk them one or two rows at a time. Finally, he can fill his silo, cutting his ensilage in the field or at his barn.

The grass farmer may plant alfalfa and mow, rake, ted, load, and bale his hay. The cotton planter can plow as he desires, plant, cultivate, and dust his crop — but he cannot, for the moment, pick his cotton mechanically. A rice farmer can use a grain binder converted for use in drenched fields. If the crop be potatoes, the farmer may plant them, cultivate them, and then dig them; or if beets, he can perform the various acts of planting and cultivation.

Each of these farmers can use horses or tractors as he pleases, and if his election should be for power farming, he can choose such a tractor as will meet the number of his acres or the type of his crop. He may haul any of his produce to market in a wagon or in a motor truck. He can grind feed for his stock or employ his winter hours in spreading manure or distributing fertilizer over his land. An engine will furnish such power as he needs. A cream separator will be at home in his dairy. He can do all this in any part of the world — and all with International Harvester machines.

This is in truth a full line of agricultural implements. But the idea of a full line was not original with the

Harvester Company. Its own first impulse had been rather to round out a cycle of production and distribution than to be able to offer any specific full variety to its customers. That thought came afterward, when the former harvesting-machine men in the field began to gain experience with the new implements they found themselves handling, and discovered that in the new lines there lay as great a chance for service to the farmer as in their traditional binders and mowers.

The addition of plows to the product of the Company added many new problems. As has been said, there is a fundamental variation between machines which work above the ground and those which dig beneath the surface. Osborne cultivators had given much education on this matter which an intimate contact with plows completed. It took the great army of Harvester Company field experts, for example, several years before they mastered completely the initial intricacies of lining up a plow for proper performance. Fortunately, they were able to bring to bear on the problem their lifelong training in service ideals. They stuck at it, and the ultimate solution came when they were able to connect up the needs of the plow with the known facts of the tractor, and to guide both with a renewed Harvester-bred conception of the service value of their work.

In 1919, Harvester also bought the Chattanooga Plow Company in order to add to its full line a chilled iron plow, a type much favored for certain difficult soil conditions. The subsequent histories of P & O and of Chattanooga plows follow parallel lines of development and improvement. The demands of Harvester's customers for equipment have, since the beginning of the industry, stressed the importance of quality. As soon as enough experience with plows had been gained to permit of critical judgment, a determined effort was made to bring the newly acquired implements up to Harvester standards. But the manufacture of plows is an intricate business, and automotive as well as implement production schemes had to be applied. Both plants were rebuilt and reëquipped, and, when their methods were secure, they were renamed Canton Works and Chattanooga Works and their product was called McCormick-Deering. All this while Harvester salesmen were acquiring plow knowledge, just as their forefathers had become skilled with the development of harvesting machinery. The progress of power farming, in itself a story so broad that it must be given separate treatment, helped; but it was at least 1925 before International's plow business had grown sufficiently to rival that of the other leaders.

It is really remarkable that the men of the Harvester Company were able to accomplish so much with plows in a few short years. They were not laboring under any threat of annihilation if they did not succeed, for even without the plow line the business was large. They were not trying to fill half-empty factories or territorial warehouses. The influences which led them so quickly to plow success were positive rather than negative. These were a recognition of the vital importance of plows to the fuller development of the practice of power farming; a desire to stand in the constructive position of being able to supply every machine need of agriculture; and an ingrained, inherited impulse to do anything that would the better serve the farmer. Such motives were not different from those which had led Harvester men willingly into the untrodden paths of the new lines.

It is well that the men who were making and selling farm equipment in the last decade of the century of the reaper had ideals and courage similar to those of their ancestors. They had lost the original binder and harvester supremacy they inherited at the time of the consolidation, just as Cyrus Hall McCormick had lost his supposed benefit of patent protection. But as he had been able to face his rivals and defeat them by means of his commercial sagacity, so their fostering of tractors and the other 'new-line' machines allowed them to replace the vanishing traditional business. They were able to face stiffening competition by the intellectual vigor of their business ability.

Harvester's post-war competitors were to prove increasingly able. Massey-Harris of Canada had been the chief rival throughout the world. It purchased an American harvesting-machine plant to permit it to manufacture in this country, and an American tractor together with its factory. The John Deere Plow Company has been the chief competitor in the United States, where its full line of farm operating equipment is made and widely sold. The J. I. Case Threshing Machine Company business flourished, based on its traditional threshers, on its quick grasp of the opportunity offered by Harvester's pioneering work in small combines, and on the ready wit with which it had first abandoned steam tractors and then kept abreast of internal combustion tractor design. With the acquisition of Emerson-Brantingham, it joined Deere and International as a full-line farm equipment company.

Deere was late in entering the tractor game, but by waiting until 1919, it missed the shocks of the war which, with the succeeding depression, wrecked such a tragic number of the smaller tractor companies. When it did so, its wide sales outlet and historic ability gave it a place next to Harvester. Oliver, on the other hand, refused to build a tractor; and so, as soon as the tractor became the hub around which the whole agricultural implement industry revolved, its business could not follow the rise of power farming. It was, however, destined to become the leading member of another full-line consolidation, the Oliver Farm Equipment Company, in which Hart-Parr furnished the tractor. Moline grounded on the shoals of 1921, got a fresh start and flourished for a period, found itself in difficulties again, and has lately been absorbed by a fifth full-line organization, the Minneapolis-Moline Power Implement Company.

Companies have risen because the agricultural implement business furnishes an inspiring challenge to men who want to leave their mark on life; companies have fallen because they have been unable to subsist on abstract rewards and because there are so many barriers on the road to success. There are extended credits, expensive service, constant change and development of machines, and the peaks and valleys of farm prosperity with which to deal. Of course there are also financial profits as well as satisfaction to seek, for the modern world is usually generous with those who render it a service. They are directly proportionate to the profitableness of agriculture itself. If farmers are prosperous, they will buy — a truism which the implement maker knows and which it might serve other city dwellers to remember who have goods to sell and who sometimes seem to underrate the relative importance of farm prosperity.

From the beginning the Harvester Company was never free from competition, nor, I think, should it have wished to be. Men develop most finely when they are spurred on by the personal competition of other men. A government rules best when the administration has to face the constructive criticism of a strong opposition. Business cannot be static: it is either growth or decay. The har-

vester war of the Eighteen-Nineties was cruel, disastrous
to the weaker combatants, and yet it was inspiring in the
way its testing brought out the finer qualities of men.
But in the first twenty International years, competition
had perhaps become routine. Henry Ford's presence in
the implement province and the new type of competition
he soon introduced returned the industry for a time to the
atmosphere of battle. War hurts, but its searing occasion-
ally furnishes an urge to continued growth.

In 1918, when he sold his first tractors in the United
States and Canada, Ford distributed them through Government agencies as a war measure. To have convinced
worried statesmen and the public that the tractor was
a new device twelve years after many tractor builders
had attained large production, and that his particular
make would prove to be the one solution of the knotty
problem of food production, was a supreme feat of salesmanship. To win the news columns of the metropolitan
press for a discussion of how the magic name of Ford
had, at a stroke, provided an answer to a supposedly
unrecognized demand for farm power, was magnificent
advertising. Whatever Ford did was deemed to be for the
real benefit of the public; and wherever he led, consumers
followed. It is therefore not surprising that his tractor
business increased by leaps and bounds.

It is questionable if the business of making tractors
would so soon have become a large-scale industry had it
not been for Ford. He taught the manufacturing world
how to combine large volume with the low-cost production methods of the automobile world. In 1918, the
manufacturing methods employed by all tractor producers were derived from implement and not automotive
standards, and they were hardly up to date in terms of
manufacturing progress. The record annual production

of four thousand Mogul 8–16's in 1915 had been non-progressively assembled; and at a period in its early existence the flywheel of the Titan 10–20 traveled exactly one mile around the factory (as compared with a subsequent three hundred feet) before it was mounted in the tractor. Some few of Harvester's factory men realized what waste there was in such methods. The production cost of a grain binder was surprisingly low, but it was a type of manufacture which required relatively little machining; and when the production methods which so cheaply produced so many implements were applied to tractors, they fell short.

During 1918 there were 133,000 tractors made in the United States. Ford had already usurped Harvester's leadership, International was second, and Case third. The expected drop in the war-time demand did not eventuate, and production mounted rapidly to the astonishing total of 203,000 machines in 1920. By this time Ford was far in the lead and was making several times as many as Harvester. For the next year or two, three-quarters of all tractors made were Fordsons. During the period of depression, sales fell off to a quarter, inventories of materials and unsold tractors were huge and high-priced, and the prospects were gloomy. Then, early in 1922, Henry Ford cut the price of tractors.

That February morning is another of the many business hours I treasure in my memory. I had taken Mr. Legge, the Company's beloved and hard-boiled general manager, on a visit to the new motor-truck installation at Springfield Works. As we were arguing some problem which then seemed to be important, the telephone rang — Chicago wished to speak to Mr. Legge. We could, of course, hear only his side of the conversation. There was much talk from the other end, and then an explosion

EARLY TYPES OF LIGHT TRACTORS
MOGUL 8–16 AND TITAN 10–20

from Alex: 'What? What's that? How much? Two
hundred and thirty dollars? Well, I'll be... What'll we
do about it? Do? Why, damn it all — meet him, of
course! We're going to stay in the tractor business. Yes,
cut two hundred and thirty dollars. Both models — yes,
both. And say, listen, make it good! We'll throw in a
plow as well!'

The meaning of this reduction in the price was that
Ford had determined to lose money in order to increase
his production. International's reply was to express a
similar (but forced) determination to meet his competition by selling at less than cost rather than to lose its
place in the business it had been pioneering. It would be
fruitless to rehearse the detailed story of the long tractor
war. Harvester was waging the battle of the implement
industry against mighty Henry Ford and the automobile.
Ford was backed by the most popular commercial name
of the time and the uncounted millions earned for him by
his epoch-making car; and he was trying to capture a
business with which he had had no previous contact.
International had on its side many years of training
gained from contact with farmers, less capital by far,
and utter inexperience with defeat. Doubtless Ford had
no overt desire to attack Harvester; for, as he said later,
he was simply trying to find out how low the price might
be at which farmers would buy tractors in quantities
equivalent to automobiles. It is possible that he had over-
estimated the tractor market. There are over six million
farms in the United States, but they cannot all of them
employ tractors to advantage. Nevertheless, he sincerely
thought that he had it in his power to make a constructive
contribution to the cause of agriculture.

The salient change devised by Ford for the tractor industry concerned itself with the method of selling. Start-

ing with the initial advantage of a low price, he cut it to a level at which he readily admitted he would lose money. But he overran his object when he gave his tractor to his car dealers to sell. The farm tractor did not originate from the automobile; it is really a member of the implement, not of the motor-car, family. Ford dealers in the country were well acquainted with their customers, but not with their farm needs; and Ford dealers in the cities had no sales outlet for farm goods. Recognizing these truths, Ford provided an industrial model of his tractor for the city trade, and made arrangements for a line of agricultural implements to meet the supposed sales needs of his rural agencies. This he did by inviting certain companies to manufacture new and light types of farm machinery specially designed to accompany his tractor.

But Ford's preparations for the provision of agricultural machinery were to prove inadequate and his mistake in this direction was one of the main reasons for his subsequent retirement, for several years at least, from the tractor business. The implements were generally planned to correspond with the size of the tractor, not for the work they had to perform. They were engineering marvels, easily manufactured and cheap to build — but they did not possess the ruggedness which ninety years of experience with agricultural equipment had shown to be necessary. Then, too, the Ford tractor itself, though it had been designed by the finest automobile brains in the world and built by the best manufacturing system in existence, was deficient from a farm point of view. It was too light to gain the traction necessary to pull the desired fourteen-inch plows. It lacked power to function in those supposedly unusual circumstances which, because of hostile Providence or the unevenness of soils, a farmer meets at least once in every round of his field. The Fordson was a perfect theoretical answer to an imperfect practical problem. It would operate successfully in so many conditions that huge numbers were sold; but it failed in so many places that ultimately farmers would have no more of it.

Harvester's answer to the Fordson attack could be made only with the old two-cylinder Titan 10–20, which even then was ready for replacement with a modern model, and the four-cylinder International 8–16. Under the terms of combat set by Ford and met by Legge, their prices were reduced to $700 and $670. A suitable tractor plow or other implement was given away with each sale. Even so, compared to Ford's price of $395, the apparent advantage was all with the champion of automobile methods.

A Harvester challenge rang through the land. Everywhere any single Ford sale was rumored, the Harvester dealer dared the Ford representative to a contest. No prizes were offered, no jury awarded merit to one or another contestant. No quarter was given and none was asked. Grimly the protagonists struggled, fiercely they battled for each sale. The reaper war was being refought with modern weapons. Supremacy in the tractor field was at stake. During the next three years there were literally thousands of these contests, and in the end Harvester won farmers back from price to its own version of quality and proved its right to survive in the tractor field. It demonstrated unequivocally that more stamina than the Fordson possessed was needed in a tractor.

The Company won many tractor trials, but its losses were large. Obviously the cut price was to meet the competition of Ford's policy of selling at less than cost and bore not the slightest relation to production costs or value. Under the influence of a tremendous sales campaign, the surplus inventory of tractors melted away. Two improved new models, the McCormick-Deering 10–20 and 15–30, were introduced which summed up the entire story of Harvester's tractor experience. Millions of dollars were poured into the modern type of labor-saving manufacturing equipment. Production costs were slashed by the means of efficiency gained through elimination of waste effort. In 1924, Harvester's tractor sales increased as the continued pressure of the many field contests began to tell. In even greater numbers farmers were coming to realize that their field requirements could not be met with less quality than the high standards Harvester was building into its machines. In 1927, the number of Mc-Cormick-Deering tractors sold passed the agricultural portion of Fordson sales. In 1928, when Ford's industrial tractor volume could no longer alone support his business, he ceased tractor production altogether.

I do not pretend that the so-called tractor war was as vital a matter for Mr. Ford as it was for the International Harvester Company. During these same years his motor-car sales were annually exceeding the million mark. However much the problem of farm power appealed to his personal interest, tractors necessarily had to be a secondary consideration with him. But they were the pivot of Harvester's entire business. The Company was fighting for its traditional position of leadership in the agricultural equipment world.

Where Harvester's plight had been uncertain in 1922, its situation in the end was one of triumph. It had proved to the world that a farm tractor should be sold as a part of a farm equipment line and should not become the minor brother of an automobile. It had taught itself how to design a better tractor than any hitherto known, and how to build it in terms of the highest art of production.

Ford had convinced thousands of horse-using farmers that in the tractor they could find the answer to their power needs. International proved to them that to do their work they must have a superior machine. When the tractor war was over, the farmers of the world appreciated beyond a shadow of doubt that they would best serve themselves by providing their farms with a tractor rugged enough to resist the shocks of farm use and powerful enough to do all of their work. They knew that there can be no such thing as a good cheap tractor.

It can be readily understood that the fighting spirit developed during the years of the tractor war, like the vigor generated by the battles of the harvester war, had a beneficial effect on every other portion of the Company's business. Nowhere was this more apparent than in foreign countries, where the battles had raged as fiercely as in the fields of Ohio or on the prairies of Kansas. Harvester was recovering as strikingly abroad as it was at home from the losses of the Great War and the depression. Standing alone, the facts of business may seem but a trite recital of mundane circumstances; but perhaps they become clothed with romance when imagination is allowed to picture their background. The tale of the exploration into the agricultural needs of far lands is not a part of this particular phase of recovery from incipient calamity, and I refer to it here merely because the power that accomplished it followed so logically as a result of the spirit of victory engendered by the tractor war. An enlargement of the domestic business resulted from exactly the same causes; but any detailed account of it must also be a subsequent part of this story of Harvester progress.

The miscellaneous items of the Company's business, such as steel and fiber, remained fairly constant, and the sale of binder twine and the old-line machines did not

increase. But the new-line implement trade flourished as
did the volume of repairs, which are the measure of the
Company's increasing ability to render service. Tractor
sales rose spectacularly from the low point of the war
with Ford. Motor trucks also enjoyed a steady increase.
The automotive lines constitute a full half of Harvester's
volume.

I cannot refrain from mentioning here one motor-
truck incident of 1921 which indicates that, however
much a renewed spirit of determination was kindled by
the tractor war, it had by no means died out before that
event. Really, Ford's attack gave a new and stronger
purpose to a great and by no means obsolete ability.

The depression of 1921 found Springfield Works carrying a large inventory of purchased motors, transmissions,
axles, and other motor-truck parts. In accordance with
another of Legge's brilliant schemes to start business
going again, these parts were assembled and sold to the
Company's own dealers at a considerably reduced figure.
The plan was to use them in a great canvassing effort
designed to start trade going. They were painted a bright
red, and were, to say the least, spectacular as they dashed
across the countryside carrying goods to farmers which
farmers would not come to town to seek. They could not
fail to bring home to agriculturists the message that
Harvester was confident of their future and its own.
Some friendly wag coined for these crimson messengers
of prosperity the homely but expressive name 'Red
Babies.' They did their work — and even to-day a farm
implement dealer's delivery truck, whatever its make or
whatever his allegiance, is called a 'Red Baby' in many
sections of the country.

Perhaps the moral of the 'Red Baby' story is that usual
business methods will not suit unusual circumstances.

The Great War and the worst depression in all commercial history could not be faced except with courage and extraordinary will to do and an illogical and superb confidence in the real nature of the veiled future. Successive attacks of the law officers of State and Federal Governments were met with the cleanest record ever made before the public by any corporation and by the whole-hearted favor of the customers whose interests those officers were supposed to represent. Tractor competition of a more serious nature than was ever known in the harvester wars of former days was turned by changed manufacturing methods and the reiterated proof of superior value. All in all, Harvester was demonstrating to the world that it had a constructive interest in the problems of the farmer, as well as the business acumen and the militant spirit necessary to fight its own battles.

CHAPTER XII

POWER FARMING

THE reaper was the first of the implements by which mechanized power was brought to the aid of agriculture. It appeared suddenly before an unexpectant world. Twenty years after its birth, it had become a proved mechanism, and in thirty years its purpose had been accepted everywhere and its usefulness was hailed by farmers and by statesmen. Then, one by one, its progeny began to appear upon the scene: the self-rake reaper, the harvester, the wire binder, and the twine binder. During the same interval human ingenuity, thus focused on the unfolding solution of the demands of mechanized agriculture, had produced the steel plow and its many descendants along a collateral line of kinship. The reaper was not their father — it was the first expression of the thought which originated them. It was an intellectually inspired reply to a want which men had long felt, but had not known how to satisfy — a reply which, when it reduced theory to practice, gave other men the mechanistic clue to other problems.

Up to the advent of the reaper, the peak load of the agricultural cycle was in the harvest. It was always easier, with the bounty of Nature and even with the crudest of tillage implements, to make a crop than to gather it. McCormick's invention, replacing the sickle, the scythe, and the cradle with a competent machine, shifted the incidence of time and labor to the turning of the soil. When the invention of the modern plow solved that problem, the peak load of farm labor rested on threshing. The early horse-power thresher then became as inadequate for its share of crop production as the primitive plow had proved in the presence of the reaper. Quickly, therefore, inventive genius gave its attention to this final phase of crop production and evolved more and more efficient types of stationary steam-power threshers. Perhaps if this process of development were searchingly analyzed, it would be made clear that the solution of one mechanical farm problem inevitably makes necessary the solution of other related needs; and therein lies the reason for the steady progress that the farm implement industry has made since McCormick opened the door to mechanized agriculture.

Within sixty years after the reaper's birth, thinkers began to ask themselves why machinery, already so adequate a substitute for the arms of men, could not be similarly applied to those tasks which were beyond the power of all muscular physique. They seized upon the principle of internal combustion, added it to the stock in trade of implement practice and produced the tractor. This was a vehicle, an element in the widening scheme of transportation, but a power plant mightier than the animal power which farmers had summoned to drag the machines that were the source of their own liberation. Thus, by the time of the reaper's eightieth birthday, its progeny, multiplied now by the succeeding generations of its fruitfulness, were growing in stature as well as in number. Machines were becoming more purposeful.

A century ago, one man with a hoe and a scythe could bend his back and tend one farm acre, or, at a stretch, a two-acre patch of land. Now, with the help of those artifacts which we, masters of a material destiny, sum up in the term 'efficiency,' he can single-handed accomplish at least a hundred acres of production. But farm power is no longer a mere substitute for the farmer's beasts of burden. It has enjoyed its own transition and has become power farming. This latter stage of development became visible by the time of the reaper's ninetieth year. As soon as the tractor could be reduced in size and cost, it became useful to the many instead of the few. A further expression of man's wants arose out of the previous answers to his quest. Why not apply the power directly to the work and let it function positively in its own way, to do the work both of the animal and the man? Search precedes science; and the final application of mechanical power to farm needs appeared when power was made an integral, rather than an incidental, part of the farm operation. Power farming, new in itself but still the latest child of the reaper, does just that.

Perhaps Cyrus Hall McCormick knew in 1831 only that he had made farm work easier and had thus permitted the production of more food. Three-quarters of the population of the Western world lived by agriculture in 1831, whereas less than one-quarter supply our present cry for bread. Undoubtedly in future years a still smaller relative number of producers will suffice. It seems reasonable to guess that, if power continues to march with progress, we may learn to be even more worthy of what the past has done. Perhaps power will give us, even more than now, material ascendancy over those problems which our fathers feared but faced.

Figures prepared by the United States Department of Agriculture show that in 1918 and 1919 there were about 26,400,000 horses, mules, and other draft animals on American farms. These dates mark the high point of animal power as applied to agriculture. They also coincide with the war-time rush to tractor power which marked the initial decline of the horse. It is not suggested that before then animals had not served their purpose. They had drawn the reaper and its progeny across the farms of the East and over the prairies, but their maximum contribution could be rendered only during the comparatively brief periods when farmers were preparing for harvest and were harvesting. During the other many months a farmer naturally had to feed his beasts or allow them to graze on land that must otherwise be unproductive. Also, horses could not be speeded beyond a certain point; they wilted under the summer heat of the Western wheat and corn climate; they tired — just as man had tired before 1831 — and they were admittedly an expensive power plant.

The Department says that in 1924, when tractors were already beginning to be effective, America's farmers annually employed a total of sixteen billion horse-power hours at a cost of three billion dollars a year. Five-sixths of this amount was paid out to keep the animal power plant in operation. Farm labor, too, was staggering in its demands upon farm income. Sixty per cent of what agriculture spends on farm operation must go for power and for labor. If the tractor satisfies farm power needs, it is also obvious that human labor is needed in inverse ratio to the supply of mechanical power. Animal power endeavored to maintain pace with the demands of farming, but it could do so no longer after 1919. In 1931, with progress still marching on into the reaper's second century, the farms of our country are, on an average, using 3,500,-000 horse-power more each year than they could or would employ before the infant appearance of the tractor. Without horse-drawn implements there would once have been an insufficiency of farm production. Without the tractor there could have been no increment to the farmer's ability to serve the world.

I do not pretend that there do not remain in the forum

of agricultural discussion men who dispute the claim of
tractor farmers that it is cheaper to farm with a tractor
than with horses. They declare that the price of horses
and mules, as well as of feed to keep them, is low. But
one thousand dollars invested in a tractor will provide
more power for ordinary work and for the peak loads
than an equivalent value of horseflesh; the tractor eats
only when it works; and the housing of a tractor (too
frequently in the open air) costs less than a barn. It
would be possible to amass statistics by the page to prove
these statements. Suffice it to say that the Department
of Agriculture estimates that a tractor drawbar horse-
power can be developed for half the cost of an animal
horse-power. But argument is no longer necessary — the
modern farmer knows. In 1929 there were only 19,000,-
000 animals employed in agriculture as compared to
26,400,000 in 1919. Then there were less than 150,000
tractors in use, while to-day there are nearly a million.

It seems probable that this generation is wisely allowing the matter of the cost of production to determine the
answer to the problem of farm power. During the last
decade of the reaper century, farmers also discovered
that a tractor would pull their implements and cultivate
their land regardless of the season; that it would work
faster than their teams and permit them to use heavier
implements; and that it would not tire under the blaze
of a prairie sun or would, if they so wished, work as faith-
fully through the night as through the day. But now this
latest machine in the train of the reaper has in its turn
affected the reaper's previous heirs. It has forged ahead,
step for step, in the endless race of progress and has produced a new line of farm equipment that matches the
tractor itself in cost reducing efficiency. The passing of
the horses has been good for the farmer's pocketbook.

TRACTOR BINDER, A ONE-MAN HARVESTING OUTFIT OPERATING
WITH POWER TAKE-OFF

STANDARD PRESENT-DAY TYPE OF TWO-PLOW TRACTOR, HERE
USED IN THRESHING

To-day he can plow for $1.25 per acre instead of $6.50; he harvests and threshes grain for 20 cents less per bushel with the combine than with the most efficient twine binder and stationary thresher. These are the power-farming methods of the new age of agriculture.

The device which marked the definite step from the mere drawbar and belt use of internal combustion in farm tasks to the present stage of power farming is called the 'power take-off.' This is a small attachment, first pioneered by the Harvester Company and now built into practically every tractor on the market, designed to effect direct transmission of power from the tractor to the implement. Nearly all farm machines, except the mold-board type of plow, the cultivator, and a few other till-age implements, have moving parts which function as the implement moves along. As long as farmers were content to have the tractor do no more than replace the team and draw the machine, these moving parts were actuated by ground traction through the forward move-ment of the machine. Mechanically, this is a roundabout method of power transmission which occasions power losses. With direct transmission through the power take-off to the operating mechanism, the loss of power is minimized, and, since the main wheel does no more than carry the weight of the machine, the implement has to resist fewer strains and can be lighter, more compact, and less expensive.

The second and latest step in the introduction of true power farming has been the development of the Farmall or all-purpose tractor. Both these epochal ideas were matured by the engineering staff of the International Harvester Company, where now resides the counterpart of that mental energy which gave the reaper to the world. The real credit for their full fruition belongs to collective thought rather than to individual genius. A business organism is as complex as life itself. Engineering specialists can improve a theory by bringing to bear on it particular knowledge of methods or materials. Factory men know how to achieve the desired result by more direct and therefore less expensive methods. Salesmen can refine or state more clearly the objective. Executives have learned to seek out for themselves the far corners of world experience and base their criticism on observation. The mechanical skill of farmers broadens as they use the tools industry makes for them. All collaborate to achieve the single end of cheaper agricultural production.

When the present all-purpose tractor was first proposed fifteen years ago, it was intended to do no more than supply a power plant to the row-crop farmer whose corn and cotton problems refused to yield to the standard type of low-hung machine. If the man who had to till the soil of the corn or cotton belts could be supplied with a tractor high enough to ride over the top of his growing crops, and with wheels so spaced that they would travel between the rows, it would be easy to pull behind it a cultivator designed for horses. As the all-purpose tractor developed, it became apparent that any such analysis bore on but the small part of the problem. Thus, as the tractor took form through its experimental years, it was found that a multiple-row cultivator, designed to withstand the comparatively mild tractive effort of animals, was not stout enough to face the steady, purposeful pull of an engine. It was also discovered that better field work could be done if the cultivator gangs were placed ahead of the operator, where he could watch their performance, than if they were dragged behind him. Lastly, it began to be apparent that the tractor designed originally for row-crop cultivation was suitable for, or adaptable to, many other tasks — indeed, to all the lighter work on the farm.

An all-purpose tractor of any make — others than Harvester's pioneer product appeared in 1929 and 1930 — must necessarily be high; therefore, it has to be light in order not to be top-heavy. As a matter of fact, tractors have been growing lighter through the years, and the most modern models weigh not over 156 pounds per developed horse-power as compared to over 500 pounds for the mammoths of the days of the Winnipeg tests. This trend has been furthered both by refinement in design and by improved wheel-lug equipment which more effectively gears the tractor to the earth. A tractor has to drag heavy, resisting loads and any wheel slippage is absolute loss; therefore, weight cannot be reduced beyond a certain point. A standard tractor must be heavy enough to do its work. An all-purpose tractor must be heavy enough in front to avoid tipping over and yet light enough to allow the navigability which row-crop cultivation demands. It must also possess a much shorter turning radius than is practicable for a standard tractor.

It may be assumed that there will always be much room in the field of power farming for the standard type of tractor. The crawler type is best for such work as excavating and for certain agricultural conditions special enough to justify its additional expense. The all-purpose tractor will plow, pull harvesting and other implements, and do belt work within the limits of the lower power occasioned by the light weight of a machine designed for the cultivating of standing crops. The standard type of tractor, whose principal aim is simply to furnish power either by its own tractive effort or by the power take-off or by the belt, will continue to find an important place in performing the heaviest tasks of farming. The large harvester-thresher favored by the Argentine rancher demands the most rugged type of tractor, as does the system of plowing employed in Canada and the American Northwest. As a matter of fact, many farmers have found it to their advantage to use both an all-purpose and a standard tractor in their work.

The harvester-thresher is the most spectacular of the instruments of power farming. An early machine of this type was introduced to serve the dry wheat districts of California and the hilly benches of the Pacific Northwest. It was a monster, made after the fashion of threshing machines, principally of wood and pulled by as many as thirty-six horses. Publications in the East were accustomed to print picturesque photographs of the huge mechanism and its long train of straining horses laboring along a wheat-sheathed hillside rising up to a crown of pines. This, the urban editors thought, was expressive of the bigness of the West; and uninstructed people used to wonder how small farms could compete with the masters of such a mechanical marvel. But the large combine, like the large tractor, was to pass into the discard before lighter, less expensive, more serviceable equipment. The empirical science of farm implement experimentation is not satisfied until it can discover how those things that are useful to the largest farmers can also be made to serve the many.

The pioneer light harvester-thresher, a product of the International Harvester Company's growing policy of serving all farmers in all their equipment needs, was introduced in 1914. Its purpose was to harvest grain in any district where the moisture content at harvest time was sufficiently low to permit threshing at the moment of cutting. Obviously any small machine can be cheaper than one of several times its size. By its use the farmers of the semi-arid prairie States were immediately enabled to accomplish the same savings in wheat production cost as the land barons of the Pacific Coast. But combining was such a radically different method that for several years they were loath to give over the time-honored methods. Also, as is invariably the case, the first machines could not have the benefit of years of study built into them. Finally, Harvester and its competitors had to combat the arguments of the millers, who claimed that grain harvested with the combine was still too full of natural moisture; and of the adherents of stationary threshing, who claimed that the new device wasted grain. But every objection was groundless. A harvester-thresher does not waste grain. As it travels through the wheat, the battered straw is blown out at the rear and any grain not properly separated is ejected with it upon the ground, where a searcher can find it. A stationary thresher's unseparated grain is blown with the chaff upon the straw pile, where, however much of it there may be, it is concealed in a growing monument of refuse. The facts of time and experience answered the objection that combined wheat was moist wheat. Then, as the years passed, the technical skill of designers and builders improved; and by the time tractors had become widely used, the harvester-thresher was able to take its place beside the binder as a fully developed machine. As its use broadened, the quantities sold increased the mass-production methods of manufacturing brought the cost down. By 1927, a very considerable, if not the largest, part of the wheat grown in Texas, Oklahoma, Kansas, Nebraska, Colorado, California, the far Northwestern States, and in Argentina was harvested with combines.

Before the day of the tractor a farmer gathered in his grain with binders, header-binders, or headers. Ever an efficient worker, he harvested by the best methods he knew. But by previous means he could do no more than gather his cut and bound wheat into shocks, whence it must be subsequently collected and hauled to the stationary threshing machine; or, when it was cut by a header, deliver it into a prepared stack. Always, until the advent of the combine, there was the separate operation of threshing to face.

ι The Department of Agriculture estimated in 1928 that, as compared with the binder, the harvester-thresher method of harvesting saved eighteen cents a bushel, including interest and depreciation on the more expensive machinery involved, and twelve cents as compared with a header. These figures are important if you consider the production of three hundred acres of twenty-bushel wheat; and they are ultra-conservative. Most farmers claim a direct saving of twenty cents a bushel for the combine. Furthermore, losses from grain knocked out of the head by the older method of harvesting and threshing are reduced by more than half. The combine also devours as much acreage in a day as the fastest tractor binder and, in the same space of time, completes every harvest operation. At one sweep the grain is cut, threshed, and cleaned, all without the necessity of hiring extra labor.

It is no more than a short fifteen years since I lived in southern Kansas and was reasonably familiar with conditions attending the harvest season there and in Oklahoma. Each morning as the end of June approached, we would read in the papers how the advancing horde of farm laborers was descending from the East upon our vicinity. Farm wives and daughters prepared huge tables and nerved themselves for hot hours of cooking for a swarm of hungry men; and they warned one another to be prepared to stay safe indoors at night. Farm men

PICK-UP DEVICE ATTACHED TO A HARVESTER-THRESHER IN
A WESTERN CANADA WHEAT-FIELD

THE HARVESTER-THRESHER IN THE ARGENTINE

anxiously consulted their local bankers for temporary loans to pay this labor. When the foreign army arrived, 'riding the rods' or preëmpting the roofs of an inbound freight, it might be prepared to work or it might not. There were groups of college boys off for a summer's spree, willing enough, but unskilled at handling countless bundles of heavy wheat into a shock, unused to breathing threshing dust for day on day. There were swarms of tramps attracted by the unsupervised nature of harvest work and the promise of pay plus country food. These the sheriff rounded up sooner or later, commandeered a passing freight, and, by dint of posse control, passed the pest along to another community. There were experienced harvest hands who followed the season from south to north, and, because they knew their jobs, commanded the full measure of their wage. Threshing succeeded cutting, and the motley harvest army would be followed by the professional soldiery of the threshing-machine crews. They, too, are gone now, swept away with the rest of the labor problem. The combine and the farmer's own will to work are sufficient for a grain-grower's harvest.

To-day, harvest means no more than longer days than usual for a farmer and his family. As the sun mounts in the white sky of a Western morning, the dew vanishes and his fields are soon dry enough for threshing. A twist of the starter crank and the tractor hums. Fifteen-year-old daughter, clad in overalls, with a wide-brimmed hat pulled down over her clipped locks and with her set little face masked with dust, rules the iron horse; her younger brother sits nonchalantly in the shade of the cab of a waiting motor truck; and father attends to the nice details of regulating the height of the cutter bar. Ever and anon he climbs to the roof of the clattering harvester-thresher to examine the 'sample' of the grain, and then, if it is not clean enough, he descends to adjust the 'wind' which blows the chaff and weed seeds out of the threshed wheat. Acre after acre the machine devours, thirty or forty before evening if the field is large enough; and when night comes, it is ready to move to the next field and do its work over again. As yet the combine has not learned to take mother's place as a home-maker; but she no longer has to labor through the night as well, in order that an imported army of harvest hands may eat. The harvester-thresher and the tractor, mightiest of the tools of power farming, have done as much for her, it seems, as for any other.

It should be remembered that the combine method of harvesting was developed for the dry-farming districts. If wheat contains more than fourteen per cent of moisture by weight, it cannot safely be binned. It will 'sweat,' and its grade, or quality, will be depreciated by the elevator man or the miller who will ultimately buy it. This moisture can be external, caused by rain or dew or the evaporation of a muddy field, or it can be internal, like the sap of a tree. Externally induced moisture seldom harms a crop and dries quickly. I have even seen Canadian wheat combined in the spring after it has lain all winter under the snow. Where the sun burns, as it does from West Texas to Montana, the internal moisture is unimportant. In Kansas, hail rather than rain is the enemy to be feared. But east of the Mississippi River, the climate has until recently been thought too humid for the harvester-thresher. There, it has been said, grain must be placed in the shock to dry before it can be threshed. Again, though, implement experimentation is coming to the aid of striving, efficient, improving agriculture.

When wheat at harvest time contains more than the

absolute maximum of moisture, it has been found that it will dry as well in a windrow as in a shock. The windrowing machine is a wide harvester equipped simply with a platform canvas and a reel. It deposits the cut grain on top of the stubble in a long windrow, where it lies safely for three days or three weeks, until it is sufficiently dry. Rain or other external moisture does not harm it, hail does not knock it out of the prone heads. Then along comes the harvester-thresher, a small model cut to suit the smaller size of Eastern farms or one huge enough to meet the larger demands of Northwestern agriculture. Now it is equipped, not with a cutter bar and a reel to do its own reaping, but with a rotating device mounted in front of the platform canvas. This device picks up the ribbon of grain from the stubble and deposits it on the canvas; and then combining proceeds as usual.

This plan, called the windrow method of harvesting, is one of the few schemes known to the mechanical world where two operations are accomplished practically as cheaply as one. The sole added cost over combining is the fuel and overhead consumed in the simple, brief operation of windrowing, and against this there is an offset. Windrow harvesting effects a considerable saving of grain even as compared with the straight combining process. Indeed, many farmers in the dryer districts have accepted this practice to gain the benefit of the almost complete insurance it provides against hail or other inclemency of weather or insect depredations, and because of its advantage in handling weedy grain. In Canada and parts of the Northwest, where rains are frequent, it is the only possible method by which the wheat-grower can secure the lower production cost permitted by the harvester-thresher and at the same time avoid having his wheat graded down because of surplus moisture.

The harvester-thresher is the reaper's latest descendant in the direct line. It is masterful because it is the dominant factor in harvesting. It is the best thing our generation has been able to do for the grain farmer. Let us, however, not be deceived by its present supremacy into overvaluation of its service to all the generations of humanity. Surely, as knowledge advances, there will some day, somewhere, somehow, be something better because the machine age is never satisfied with itself. The combine produces results where even the tractor binder falls short; and the windrow-harvester seems to give promise that future combines will be able to do their work where the natural moisture which nurtures growing things now appears to command a halt. But perhaps we men of to-day, farmers and manufacturers alike, will scheme out a better way. We will if we can!

Most assuredly we will if we regard the reaper's first appearance on the scene in its proper light. The harvester-thresher has cut the direct cost of harvesting to less than half, and it has eliminated the problem of outside labor — but it cannot be said to be a greater step in advance than was the original reaper over harvesting by hand. Nor, in spite of its greater worth, can it be said to possess a greater value to society than the first crude machine which started the trend toward mechanistic agriculture that has ultimately developed the combine. How slothful we would be if, given all the knowledge and progress that has followed after the reaper, we could not have made a harvester-thresher! Even in planning it we have turned to 1831 for guidance. A hundred years have passed and we have yet to find a flaw in those old seven elements upon which the first reaper was based.

The first harvester-thresher included every one of these elements in its ultra-modern structure. It had a reciprocating knife, guards in front of the blade, a reel, a platform, a main wheel, the principle of cutting to one side of the implement, and the outside divider. The harvester-thresher of to-day, new instrument of power farming that it is, actuates its moving parts, not by the main wheel drive from the ground, but by a power take-off from the tractor or by a separate engine. That, however, is no new principle of mechanics; it merely calls to the aid of the reaper's latest heir a system of propulsion, the first rudiments of which were not even dreamed of until forty-five years after the reaper's birth. Harvester men are proud of the achievements of their colleagues who scheme out artifacts of such real service to agriculture — they can be prouder still of the invention which, a century ago, made modern agriculture possible.

I have called the harvester-thresher the most spectacular achievement of power farming. It is possibly less fundamentally significant than the many implements that, usually in the form of attachments, are now appearing in the wake of the all-purpose tractor. It may be remembered that power farming is a later step in advance of tractor farming, in that it applies tractor power directly to the work and does not merely use the tractor as a better team. With the very recent advent of the all-purpose type of tractor, it was natural to plan implements which would directly suit the tractor.

The first of these machines, as has been said, was a multiple-row cultivator. This began as a two-row device and has lately been extended to span four rows. Other work was studied and satisfactory types of horse-drawn machines were reconstructed to suit new conditions. Corn and cotton planters have been attached around the all-purpose tractor in the fashion of cultivators. Corn pickers are built upon its sides until the power unit is almost concealed within the farm implement to which it is applied. A new type of potato digger, which could not otherwise have existed, is operated by the power take-off. Certain plows are coupled closely to the tractor so that the plow beams become almost an integral part of it. Wheelless mowers with long cutter bars have been designed to fit it and to take advantage of its quick-turning ability. All the machines made to be pulled by any tractor can, within the limit of its power, be towed as successfully by the all-purpose model as by the standard. The style of farm equipment is rapidly becoming changed.

Fifteen years ago, when the small tractor first appeared, it may have been thought that the new device was just a superior horse. Like the horse, it was hitched in front of the implement and set to work. But consider what happened when a binder, designed to operate at a speed of one-and-three-quarters miles per hour, was called upon to travel as much as three miles an hour. The bearings had more and faster work to do; they failed, as did the chain which actuated the binder's many sprockets, and had to be replaced with high-duty bearings. Consider also the fact that when a slow-moving, horse-drawn plow struck a concealed rock, the sensitive animals stopped; but the tractor forged on, with the result that the plow beam bent. Tractors have compelled manufacturers to heat-treat beams in order to gain added strength without added weight; and, similarly, to heat-treat harrow disks to give them added life under the stress of severer work.

The tractor has thus brought into being a higher type of farm implement, more nearly suited to its own modernity. An implement designed to operate by tractor power must be stronger, and therefore more expensive, than one designed solely for horse draft; but it is more pro-

FARMALL TRACTORS CULTIVATING COTTON AND PICKING CORN

ductive, does better work, and is cheaper in the end. It
is a finer implement to match the quality of modern
farming. Of itself, regarded merely as a substitute for
animal traction, the tractor would have induced a re-
designing of farm equipment. Now the all-purpose
tractor has come as well, and again the experimental
work of adapting old machines or producing new types
goes forward.

The horse is by no means a bygone power plant, however much he may have vanished from the thousands of
American horseless farms. He must continue to serve
those farmers on the economic fringe who are just able to
pull through and whose operations cannot afford to sustain an investment in modern equipment. He will survive
long in those backward countries, where, because of a
low standard of living, labor is cheap. He may live long-
est in the crowded communities of the Orient, where
animals as yet are possessions of the rich alone and
where hand harvesting is still the order of the day. But
the Orient is not all overpopulated; there are five horseless farms in Indo-China. In any country there are farm
tasks that no horse is strong enough to do, and these
demand the tractor. In any country which seeks to
release the brains of its citizens from the deadening
burden of toil, power farming reigns.

The motor truck, too, has come to take its place as a
proper instrument of power farming. Threshed wheat,
for example, is customarily poured from the harvester-
thresher's storage tank into a motor truck and wheeled
away to the railside grain elevator. Urban needs require the transportation of heavy, concentrated burdens,
whereas farms demand speed and instant service. Therefore, the Harvester Company's truck stations in the rural
districts concern themselves mainly with the distribution

of the lighter models. The servicing of motor trucks has become well-nigh as important a function of the harvest season as the servicing of harvesting machinery.

The purpose of all these power achievements of the modern age of agriculture is to make better farming possible. The average factory makes a better quality product because of modern equipment than with the hand methods formerly employed. The average farmer does his work more in harmony with the standards of to-day's demands for quality with machinery than without it. But, just as it is probable that the principal objective of mass production is to reduce the cost of manufactured articles, even so is it certain that lower farm production costs are the main benefit of power-farming equipment. Wheat farmers of the West are aided by cheap land, but it is the machinery of power farming that has allowed them to cut the cost of raising their crops. The all-purpose tractor methods of corn cultivation are still new, yet in Iowa and Nebraska farmers are claiming savings more than sufficient to pay for their power farming equipment in a single year. Cotton planters in the better districts, where fields are large enough to permit batteries of tractors and their attachments to operate, can bring their crop to the picking stage for considerably less than half the cost of their old methods. Whether legislation succeeds in solving the problem of farm prosperity or not, power farming has provided a sure way to reduce farm production costs.

The tractor and its attached implements will unquestionably permit larger farms. The story of hand labor was want — the story of machinery is plenty. Within the reaper century farmers have advanced themselves into a realm of undreamed-of power. An engineer has computed that the United States does thirty-four times as much work by means of machinery as by hand; whereas China, at the opposite end of the scale, performs four-fifths of its labor manually. America is efficient because of the faith it has reposed in mechanical instead of muscular effort. Our farmers are more efficient than the average of men. They demand the equipment that will allow them to extend the power of their arms. Before the reaper, one man could work, at the most, a two-acre patch of wheat, while with the instruments of power farming, individual productivity is multiplied a hundred fold. Farms have grown in size because of available horse-drawn machinery. Why should there not be, in the future, still larger farms, as large as the farmer's machine-backed physique and machine-directing brain can command?

Power farming has brought many social advantages to agriculturists. It has given them a broader individualism. Its rapid pace has discovered new leisure for them within the hours of the year to do those things which could not be included in the dawn-to-dawn labor of the erstwhile farm day. They have gained knowledge how to acquire and use those conveniences and privileges, the radio and the State University, which were formerly beyond their reach. All these attributes have combined to widen the intellectual horizon of the farmer. Individualism, leisure, and knowledge are an immediate assistance toward a better life, and they also multiply their fruits. I do not say that the readjustment from ancient to modern ways is easy, or that power farming has been the sole cause of farm progress. Rather, farmers have wanted betterment and so have created a demand for the tools of modernism. But without them, without power farming, they would have asked in vain.

It is the European habit to remain truer to traditional

methods than in America, where our nervous idealism is ever searching for something new. Thus, farmers in the Western Hemisphere have been largely willing to adapt their land to machinery. European agriculture is more provincial. Adherence to local tradition has asked that machinery be adapted to favored local methods of plowing, of cultivating, and of harvesting. Individual selection — which is different from individualism — is prevalent in Europe's every attitude toward industry and is a reason why mass production and its benefit of lower price have not flourished there. To a certain extent this is justified by the minute accuracy of the work that Europe is unwilling to entrust to machinery. Perhaps tractor attachments will solve those problems; or perhaps Continental peasants will see from afar the liberation America's machinery has wrought for her farmers and will demand that they too be freed. Perhaps, even, the European consumer will offer his producer a higher standard of living in return for a cheaper price. It is not so long since the invention of the spade and the scythe eliminated three-quarters of the labor bill of soil preparation and harvesting. In the last century the efficiency of farm production has been increased from thirty to a hundred times. There is room in the achievements of these rapid days of ours for hope for the farmers of all the world.

Of course, there will be improvements in the instruments of power farming. Oil or alcohol may reduce the tractor's fuel bill, more refined tractor attachments may succeed in applying power more directly or more usefully to farm work, scientific farming methods will play an increasingly important part. In the future, octogenarians will doubtless say, as the old guard says to-day, 'We worked a lot harder in those early days.' To be sure —

they used muscle where we are using mind; but perhaps
some future man will be able to demonstrate that 1931
did not realize, as another century may do, how best to
summon abstract forces to his aid. But we, I think, have
done reasonably well. Consider the case of a friend of
mine, whom I will call Mr. Highouse of the West: He
settled in Madison County in 1864, a boy with the world
before him waiting to be conquered. He turned the
prairie sod with a team of oxen and harvested his first
wheat with a cradle. Then he used a reaper; and then,
one by one, the successively improved generations of
the reaper's labor-saving children and grandchildren.
Finally, the harvester-thresher appeared upon the scene.
Highouse was old by then and his descendants harvested
in his place. In 1865, he and his like had spent three days
of man-labor to reap and thresh an acre of grain. In
1929, he watched his young grandson cut and thresh
thirty acres in a day. One lifetime spans the magnificent
transition from cradle to combine. I wonder what farming will be like a hundred years from now?

CHAPTER XIII

THE DISTRIBUTION OF FARM EQUIPMENT

A MODERN corporation engaged in supplying an essential product can, if it be favored with a public demand, enjoy the privilege of success; but by the same token it cannot escape responsibilities. These responsibilities are heavy when its position is that of a leader, for the public must be served. Such a modern sentiment has for all time been the watchword of the entire agricultural implement industry. Cyrus Hall McCormick felt it subconsciously as he was developing the many phases of his system of distribution; his successors and the successors of his rivals patterned their methods after his; and the men of this generation follow practices which are nothing more than growth from ancient roots. I suppose that to-morrow will be a development from 1931, that it will improve, and that it will be true, as to-day is true, to the traditions of the past.

It will be remembered that in the early days of the reaper, McCormick appointed general agents whose duty it was to travel over the country supervising the work of local agents who in turn appointed subagents to contact with the farmer. These last were country merchants, crossroad blacksmiths, and even, in some cases, rural postmasters. They were the forbears of the dealer of to-day; but in the time of the early reaper, it was the local agent and not the subagent who carried repair parts and such stocks of machines as his territory demanded. There were no company-owned branch houses, and a surprisingly large part of each year's volume of machines was shipped from the factory in the weeks immediately preceding harvest.

One of the greatest elements of service that the modern agricultural implement industry has been able to perfect for its customers has been the development of a far-flung system of branch houses. It has been related how the local agent of Civil War times gradually became a jobber, and how, when a manufacturer had sufficient capital himself to control distribution as well as production, territorial business was placed in the hands of a resident manager. The usual title given this man by the McCormick Harvesting Machine Company and its competitors was that of 'general agent' (because, though his field of operations was more limited, his duties coincided with those of the original general agents). The International Harvester Company naturally fell heir to the nomenclature as well as the employees of the constituent companies. But with the growth of the business, due first to new lines and then to tractors, the head of a territorial division became less an agent and more an executive in his own right; so in 1917 his title was changed to 'branch manager.'

The typical personnel of a branch has followed the original lines, but naturally it is much larger now than in the old days. The field staff is traditionally built up of 'blockmen,' who do business with the several dealers in a predetermined subdivision of the branch territory, and of salesmen, or canvassers, who work with the dealer and lend him skilled selling assistance in his contact with the farmer. The dealers are more machinery-conscious now than in former years, and they find it to their advantage to do much of the work of setting up machines newly received from the factory or the branch warehouse, and of the servicing of minor complaints. The farmer is also a far cleverer mechanic than was formerly the case and has grown accustomed to do himself many of the servicing jobs that were once done for him. Therefore, the branch manager's force of field experts is smaller — and more skilled — than it used to be.

These three ranks of field men, the blockmen, the salesmen, and the service men, constitute the infantry of the Harvester army. They were the ones who carried out the orders of their captains and fought the harvester war; they were the ones who staged the demonstrations which won the tractor war; they are the shock troops, brave and skilled and determined, who lead every advance toward wider sales or deeper service. I have been one of them, and from them I learned to make my theoretical, inherited ideals practical, to realize how the great business entity must fail to function, however sound its heart, if its hands be not willing and able. Numberless tales of self-sacrifice and devotion might be linked to their personalities. I choose but one for record here.

One day, when I was a very new and self-important general agent in southern Kansas, a farmer called on me. Because he respected the Harvester Company and wished it well, he came to tell me how one of my salesmen was wasting Company time. 'I was plowing when he came to my farm and tried to sell me a spreader. I told him I didn't want one, so he said he'd help me plow. Well, he did, and the afternoon went on, so I invited him to stay and eat. After supper he wanted to talk spreader again — to tell me what it would do to pep up my soil. So it got kind of late and I asked him to spend the night. Next morning he started in to talk spreader again, and when I shut him up, he said he'd help me do my chores and then we'd plow some more. So, just to get rid of him, I bought the damn spreader. Say, Mac, how soon can I get it? — he sure got me all hopped up on how I can build up my field! But he sure wasted a lot of time on one little sale!'

Perhaps. Perhaps he also earned that farmer one or two bushels more of corn to the acre and made him the price of the machine in the year. Perhaps, also, he was the spiritual heir of D. R. Burt, who fought Manny in Iowa and 'sold twenty machines.' Burt lived sixty years before my salesman, but unless I am much mistaken, the breed has not yet died out. The objective of the attack has changed — that is all. Competitors still strive with each other, but not in the same 'cut-throat' way — they fight for better agriculture.

The old-time blockman had to concern himself with a relatively simple line of harvest tools. Now, however remarkable may be his knowledge of the multitude of machines in his catalogue, he can no longer be a specialist in all of them. Thus, special travelers have come into being, men recruited mainly from the ranks of the block-men, who travel over the territory of one or several branches to bring their specific knowledge of cream separators or engines or motor trucks or other lines to bear on local problems. These specialty men frequently operate under the control of specialty managers in the home office whose duty it is to supervise the distribution of some particular class or product rather than to follow the progress of the Company's entire line, as do the regular departmental managers. The ramifications of Harvester's full line are so many that there is room for specialization even at the top of its trained sales force.

The most complete segregation between classes of product is in the case of motor trucks. Many excellent implement men make but inferior automotive salesmen and many highly successful truck mechanics are not temperamentally suited for direct dealings with farm psychology. Therefore, in certain instances there has been effected an almost complete separation of the motor truck from the implement staff. The motor-truck personnel is usually housed on the branch property, frequently in a separate building; but if the warehouse itself is not well situated for motor-truck sales, it carries on in a service station placed in the center of truck activity in the city in question. In the metropolitan areas, as for example in New York, where there is no chance for agricultural implement sales, the motor-truck branch is entirely independent and self-contained.

The branch manager has an assistant to aid him in the conduct of his affairs. Both of these men travel widely over the territory and supervise all sales problems. As in the case of every business anywhere in the world, the boss cannot hope to sit at home at his desk and regulate distribution by correspondence. He must know his machines and, what is far more important, know his customers — and to perform either of these intricate tasks adequately, he must travel nearly as much as the blockman. He gains an independent judgment of crop conditions, is in touch with rural opinion, and himself helps carry to the dealer and to the country what message he can of the labor-saving, profit-producing feats of mechanized agriculture.

What men they were and are, these general agents of the old days and these branch managers of more recent times! To select one from among those I know who are gone or are living in well-earned ease among the orange groves of Southern California would be an injustice. There are too many others whose exploits have passed my notice because the days of 1931 are too crowded with the business of the present to give due consideration to the foundations upon which our work is reared. The men of the old days poured their sweat upon the land to further the cause of reapers and harvesters and binders;

and in so doing they showed us the way to combines and tractors. They stood beside my grandfather and my father. They worked with them to take a load off the backs and straining arms of farmers in order to let us show agriculture how to find leisure by means of thoughtfully planned work.

I cannot find it in me to do less than pay due honor to the past. It is the foundation stone of our existence. There would have been no chance for the brilliant young executive of to-day to be manager over the sales destinies of a force of fifty men if the general agent of twenty years ago had not been master of the details of Harvester's few old lines. We who are the younger generation are false to their charge to us if we do not improve. We fall short if we merely grasp at their heritage. Branch managers are general agents, changed not in title only, but in fact. We ride on the wings of power farming where they first taught the fledgling how to fly. We are efficient because they first showed the farmer how to think in terms of machinery. We serve in a wider sense because they lifted for us a corner of the veil of the future.

In his work to-day the branch manager has the ready assistance of a branch advertising man. Where Cyrus Hall McCormick and his contemporaries were accustomed to write their own advertising copy, rightly believing that they, the heads and frequently the originators of their businesses, knew more than other men about such few machines as they had to sell, advertising is now a specialized science. There is a large department at the home office to prepare copy for magazine and newspaper advertisements, catalogues, and the many mailing folders favored by the publicity system of the implement industry. The branch advertising man sells publicity in the same way that the blockman sells contracts. Advertising is nothing if it is not an aid to salesmanship; and a system of distribution which fails to link the personal message of the printed page with the personal persuasion of the spoken word, falls short of its mark.

Included in the staff of a branch house is, of course, an office manager, who in the days of the past used to be the cashier who kept the accounts. There is also a credit manager to keep in touch with the financial stability of potential customers before a sale is made. In certain districts there is a collection manager who handles, generally for several adjacent branches, such time paper as may accompany the settlement of a contract. There is the service manager whose duty it is to supervise all forms of territorial service work. Finally, there is the repairs foreman, as important a factor and as representative of Harvester's ideals as any man on the branch manager's staff. He it is who presides over the long rows of tiered wooden bins — steel in the most recently constructed buildings — and furnishes spare parts as readily for an 1899 mower as for a 1931 harvester-thresher.

I do not think that the Harvester Company distributing system which I am describing differs widely from that of its main competitors except in size. No company can hope to be really effective in the agricultural implement industry unless it is prepared to cover fully as much of the territory as it plans to serve. Many organizations are not nation-wide; and yet they can make their sales pressure felt in the given district in which they choose to operate. Of course you must assume that any one who desires to do business with farmers should have in his hands a manufactured article that contains no surplus dollar of price-raising cost. If he wishes to do a repeat business, he must have first designed and then built quality into his product, for the farmer is a keen buyer, quick to criticize and willing to change if his conceptions of machine service are not met. Above all, he must realize that the machines he is selling are planned to do necessary, unavoidable work — and work is the real root of service.

The larger part of the system of Harvester branches lying across North America was originally developed by the McCormick and Deering Companies before 1902. In a few locations the Champion or the Osborne building was more desirable, and when P & O was acquired, it brought with it several fine warehouse properties. Of course the consolidation resulted in the disposal of certain branches; and when the inflated condition of the old harvesting-machine lines was appreciated, it was found that others could be consolidated without injury to the business or hardship to customers. The natural increase in volume through the years has required additional sales points where the trade in a district could be more intensely cultivated to advantage. Much of the recent increased business has developed in the West — in particular in the dry-farming sections — and new distributing centers have been provided wherever required. The skeleton of the distribution system is flexible and has been kept in constant balance with the status of the business. Its object has been to supply agricultural implements to farmers where and when they need them.

The original type of branch warehouse has not proved suitable for the storage of the bulkier types of new power machinery. Formerly farm equipment could invariably be shipped from the factory to the country in disassembled units. Such integral parts as wheels and poles could be packed together in a freight car and the main parts of the machine could be nested in crates. A six-foot grain binder, for example, reaches the dealer in thirteen separate shipping packages. All these parts could easily be stored in tiers in any available type of building. Thus an implement warehouse of the time-honored variety was most frequently a multiple-story building conveniently located with regard to railway switching, more or less without concern for any other than railway accessibility.

The advent of trucks, tractors, harvester-threshers, corn pickers, and other large machines has furnished for farm use a type of implement complicated enough to require the most highly skilled assembly. The retail dealer or even the individual farmer can set up a binder or a mower or a plow, but the mechanical requirements of tractor or truck assembly can be better and more cheaply accomplished in a factory organized for repetitive operations. Therefore, the most modern types of power machinery are sent out to the country as complete (in the case of the tractor) or as nearly complete (in the case of the combine) machines. They are transportable on their own wheels and can be more readily stored on one level than on the floors of a multiple-story building. Crated implements can be packed away just as easily in such a structure as in the traditional type of warehouse. Thus the modern implement storage building has become a one-story type of structure.

Another cogent reason for this has been the great increase in the construction cost of buildings. A business dealing with the necessities of life cannot afford to burden its prices with a single unnecessary penny of direct cost or overhead expense. Thus, when a new warehouse has to be built, the type to be selected will obviously be an inexpensive sheet-iron or similar building built on reasonably cheap land rather than a comparatively costly mill-construction or concrete structure located in the crowded heart of a city's wholesale district. It is cheaper to put up such a building as well as more convenient.

The present-day model of implement warehouse has also been materially affected by the wide spread of automobile and motor-truck transportation. A retail dealer, whose store was situated twenty or thirty miles from a branch house, used to receive his supply of implements by local railway freight. He would either have to anticipate most of his year's requirements to make up a mixed car at the branch warehouse, or pay the added freight for less-than-carload shipments. Nor could the railways provide expeditious transportation on their minor rural lines. The motor truck has come forward to solve these problems, and an important number of machines are now delivered from the company branch to the retail distributor by highway instead of by rail. The 'Red Baby' taught the dealer, not merely to carry implements for sale and service out to the farmer, but also to use road transportation to connect himself more directly with his source of supply.

The shipping platforms of a modern implement warehouse must therefore face the dusty highway as well as the rails leading away to the factory. At harvest time the red truck will be there, and beside it will be a farmer's automobile or truck. He has come to town to secure some unusual repair part which the large branch stock will provide, or to visit the new show room to inspect there some new type of implement that he has seen advertised, or which has been of service to a neighbor. When the farmer drove a buggy, he could not spare the time to trot twenty-five miles to town; but to-day distance is a matter of less importance. Therefore there is a growing and more friendly contact, engendered largely by the branch repairs room and the sample floor, between the ultimate consumer and the Company's territorial warehouse. Where the branch used to be no more than a

depot close to an agricultural district for the temporary
storage of goods in transit from factory to farm, with
incidental offices for the sales force, it has now become
more vital. Its show room is an attractive place where
the entire locally used line may be displayed. Its formerly unvisited repairs department has been moved from
the fourth floor to a space immediately behind the sample
room, where its impressive stock of spare parts may
serve as an assurance of instant service. The branch has
become the center of a radiating farm equipment activity.

All this has resulted in solidifying the contact between
the individual farmer and the company which serves him.
And yet, if the branch house has become the center of the
territorial system, the newly developed distributing con-
tacts have strengthened, not the International Harvester
Company alone, but the retail dealer as well. His business has also developed and kept up with the times. He
has changed from a small agent for machinery sold on
commission into an independent merchant. Much has
been written and said about the precarious state of the
country implement dealer. Fifteen years ago one out of
every four failed each year — but that was when most
farm equipment distributors were small and weak. Then,
the old-line machinery in the agent's store belonged to
the company for which he handled it and, unless he could
prevail upon his customers to pay him a premium because
of the special service he could render them, he could not
hope to earn more from his efforts than a mere commission. Such a thing as a dealer who sold farm equipment
exclusively was almost unknown. No company had a
really full line; and the local agent had to bolster up his
business with hardware, furniture, funeral direction, and
the like. I do not mean to say that in isolated communities where stores are few or in districts where agri-

culture is not a major industry, a dealer does not still have to resort to other merchandise to round out twelve months of selling effort and income. Nevertheless, I am satisfied that, wherever circumstances permit, an implement dealer best serves his own interests — to say nothing of those of the farmer — if he is able to concentrate his attention on the business of providing his community with farm operating equipment.

Many an old-time implement dealer's store was housed in a dilapidated frame building decorated with a faded sign informing the street in front of him as to his whereabouts. Dusty bins along one wall contained nails and screws, tin cups and hinges, or porcelain pans and aluminum kettles. A glass case exhibited a shotgun or two, some ammunition and cutlery. Toward the rear, a broken package of brooms sprawled over a partly assembled cream separator. His desk, marked principally by a legion of advertising calendars, was littered with papers, unmailed bills, and mislaid notices of cash discounts which prompt attention might have secured. Other racks held his disordered stock of implement repair parts. Repairs for the old harvesting lines which, like the parent machines, were sold on commission alone, were tossed in some dark corner, waiting. Too frequently the dealer himself waited for business to come to him or for the canvasser from the branch to arrive and, by force of superior persuasion, drag him out into the country. Implements were exhibited in disused barns or on adjacent vacant lots.

Lest any one think this is too dreary a picture of the past, let me say that it is drawn from my own sales experience, not with the best dealers, it is true, but with the average. In 1915, though we still used to sit around the stove in winter and gossip about a thousand other things than business, the transition toward modern methods was already beginning to be apparent. We implement men were ourselves learning what a vital sales asset neatly organized repair bins could be; and the home office was beginning to criticize the large repair inventories which showed on our books, and which were useless because so many forgotten or obsolete parts reposed in the dark corners of the dealer's shed.

Automobile salesmen were clamoring for glass-windowed show rooms to shelter and exhibit their shining cars. The merchants of a village were learning the commercial value of an ordered street. Attractive advertising literature was making it seem desirable to display machines attractively. Implement dealers' associations were preaching the keeping of accurate accounts and a more accurate knowledge of the cost of retail distribution; and they were urging manufacturers to allot more territory to an agent and so give him an adequate field in which to operate. Our developing line of machines was every year causing us to feel a growing pride which we were passing on to the dealer. Farmers were asking more questions and, as they became better farmers under the touch of the widening influence of the agricultural colleges, were demanding more mechanical instruction.

The twentieth-century flowering of American industry has not come suddenly. It has been a gradual and therefore a sure growth. The retail agricultural implement dealer has been a vital part of it. He came into existence first as a pioneer who, armed with vigorous enthusiasm instead of cash capital, followed the first farmers into the prairies of the young West. There, because he was the only merchant for miles around, he sought to purvey to all their needs. As more agricultural machinery was produced, he turned certain of his activities over to the general merchant and to the country grocer. Then came the harvester war of the Eighteen-Nineties; and the too-intense competition of that day caused his kind to multiply until, just as there were too many grain binders, there were also too many harvesting-machinery dealers. To supply the several companies' demands for distributing centers, the curbstone dealer, this time no pioneer, re-appeared in the picture. After the formation of the International Harvester Company, when the saturation point of the old harvesting-machine lines had been reached, the declining farm demand brought production under control. Then, because there were still too many dealers, their vitality was sapped and they sagged back into desuetude. Their proper position has lately been reconstituted, partly by the advance of modern methods in the implement industry itself, partly by the onward surge of modern life.

Of these two causes, the latter was undoubtedly the more important. The things one industry does are but reflections of the times; and yet the customs of our times are nothing more than the product of our thoughts. So it is possible that the developing policies of the International Harvester Company, touching so intimately such a large portion of the people, may well have helped along the modernization of agricultural life. It is certain that they did so in the case of the Nation's implement dealers. At least they helped to clothe the retailer with the first garments of his present independence.

As has been said, the early Harvester sales contracts were all of the commission variety. That is to say, the Company retained the ownership of the machines until the consummation of the retail sale and, though no retail price was named in the contract, retained a nominal control of the implement through the actual possession of the

farmer's note given in settlement of the transaction. As
the new lines were added one by one, the dealer gained
a need of property independence due to the fact that
manure spreaders, cream separators, tillage tools, and the
like were made the subject of outright sale. That this
could be accomplished was doubtless partly a reflection
of the agricultural prosperity that accompanied the advancing years of the twentieth century. Still, the practice also marked the transition of the dealer from a mere
agent of the manufacturer into a merchant doing business
on his own account.

In 1908 nine-tenths of the Company's contracts were
of the commission variety. As the relative importance of
the old harvesting-machine lines declined, the business
became more and more centered on the new-line, sales-
contract plan; and in 1917 the commission form of contract was entirely abandoned. The reaction among the
great body of dealers was immediate. At a stroke they
achieved complete control of their own affairs and became
individuals instead of agents. It is possible that no man
can attain mental ascendancy without financial independence. Dealers now do a large and a better business. However much the growth of the tractor, and in certain cases
the motor truck, may have aided, I am sure that the intellectual stimulus provided by financial independence or
the real hope of it has been the major reason. Dealers
have become thinking individuals, business men in their
own right.

Consider the fervor with which the International
Harvester Company's dealers took hold of the 'Red
Baby' campaign. Like the rest of the population of the
country, the farmers were engaged in a buyers' strike and
the mere fact of lowered prices failed to attract them.
But the better dealers, equipped now with crimson

motor trucks, loaded machines into them and toured their districts searching more intensively than ever before for sales outlets. They carried their cream separators and cultivators and feed grinders to the country, set up and ready to operate. They themselves worked the implements on a farmer's premises, and they proved to him that, depression or no, he needed this equipment in order to continue his service of supplying food to the world.

The Harvester Company's existence depends upon its ability to serve the farmer. The dealer distributes this service, acts as a channel of contact between the supply and the demand. The farmer himself holds a place in civilization proportionate to his ability to serve. These axioms are nothing but a picture of the interlocking requirements of modern life and the economic dependence of individuals — and nations — upon the service of a neighbor.

The typical implement dealer of to-day is housed in a brick building which yields nothing in attractiveness to the automobile shop front. The Harvester branch office itself has become, not a hidden-away structure with narrow warehouse windows, but a place where the Company's products may be seen and, because it is willing to express its pride in them, appreciated. The dealer has followed suit. His wide windows protect and reveal the tractors or the cream separator or the corn sheller or the binder twine which are the seasonal expression of his interest in the cause of agricultural equipment. His repair parts, which are his property and his stock in trade, are neatly housed in ordered bins where their presence may act as a visible proof of his ability to meet the exigencies of wear-and-tear and work. His desk itself is organized, and every possible discount is in his bank. He is a business man. Therefore, like the Harvester branch manager, he is to be most frequently found, not in his place of business, but in the country, drumming up sales, sensing the needs of farmers, promulgating the message of mechanized agriculture.

Any such sales system as I have described, built upon the frame of so many branch houses throughout the country and manned with a personnel whose traditions are those of service, whose practice in life is that of a fair fight, and whose object is success through progress, must necessarily depend much upon the strength of individualism. The dealer, dependent though he may be for his well-being upon the strength of the parent company, cannot profitably order machinery he cannot sell. The farmer, greatest of all individualists in the world, cannot buy equipment unless through its use he can make a profit. With all the best will possible, neither branch manager nor dealer nor farmer is able to forecast absolutely the moods of fickle Nature. Bad weather may ruin the promise of adequate sunshine or rain; or a clement harvest season may redeem incipient disaster. Individualism itself is an uncertain science; and when to it are added the uncertainties of climate, prediction of the volume of business to be expected becomes too much a matter of luck.

Hence the Harvester Company requires these many storage depots spread abroad across the land. Behind them are the huge warehouses of the factories; and in between are six great so-called transfer warehouses where machines are pooled to await the unexpected demand for last-minute shipments that seldom fails to eventuate somewhere. The Company maintains a department to keep track of machines in storage, to keep account of repairs, and to anticipate the manufacturing demands

TYPICAL FARM-IMPLEMENT DEALERS' STORES — ON THE
CANADIAN FRONTIER AND IN THE DEVELOPED SOUTHWEST

as far as may be. But the successful functioning of the system depends upon an understanding of farm conditions. If a dealer's motor truck is driven up to the branch house the day before a farmer wants a new grain binder or a tractor to save his crop, it must be filled. The Harvester Company must remain true to its ideals of service and must help that farmer perform his service to the world.

The system of distribution is largely the same in Canada as in the United States, but with due regard to the comparative youth of Canadian agriculture. The first branch house was opened by McCormick in Winnipeg in 1887. Shortly after the amalgamation of 1902, the new lands of the West began to attract settlers, farming began to penetrate another wilderness, and Harvester stood ready again to carry instant aid to the distant community of pioneer farmers. Because of the efforts of men who built their sod homes on the prairies and in the timbered fringes of the North, machinery men leaped to follow the advance guard of Northwestern agriculture. They rode the biweekly train to Edmonton, just as they had once gone out on the Union Pacific to the West and as they are now carrying implements by the waterway to Peace River. The Canadian Northwest prospered until the boom began. Then, as happens in every boom, speculators grew rich and soon crashed. Farmers were affected and bought supplies of all kinds for which they had no need — mammoth tractors, for example, whose utility could be measured only in terms of the broad horizon.

The collapse of the boom could not affect the basic wealth of Canada. Ontario had to a certain extent equipped itself with the accouterments of industry, but the foundation of Canadian prosperity is agriculture. In its train have marched Harvester's branch houses, its blockmen, its army of dealers, and its open hand of service to the farmers of the North.

Across the waters, too, the Harvester Company has followed the trail of agriculture. The McCormick Company, first in Odessa, established its own branches wherever possible. The Deerings, strong in production but not such keen salesmen, tried to meet their rivals with an army of jobbers. Thus, precedents and preferences were established which have required the Company to maintain the separate identities of McCormick and Deering machines in Europe (where the trade is now partly supplied by the European factories) and in South America. But the jobbers bought for cash no more than they could resell in the same way. Therefore, the weak type of jobber who existed before 1902 has given way to the foreign branch. Yet much of the International's foreign business is with certain jobbers, strong firms which possess an unequaled ability to serve agriculture in their districts. They have learned Harvester methods from Harvester men.

It is a tribute to Harvester Spirit that so many non-Americans all over the world, the personnel of the far-flung system of distribution, have become so finely imbued with the ideal of the American agricultural implement industry. It has gripped them in the distant pastures of Europe, where, in a dozen different languages, they are spreading the gospel of better agriculture. South America knows it, and South Africa — Egypt, too, and the dry hills of North Africa. Cold Manchuria and the tropical Philippines are experiencing the benefits of Harvester service. Its message is old in Australia and New Zealand and new in the islands and the tropical lands along the antipodean equator. India and China, in spite of their millions, are turning to farm power to accomplish those farm tasks for which the millions are too weak. Everywhere under the sun where agriculture exists, there is also a nucleus of Harvester service — everywhere except in Russia. Even there Harvester machinery is busy; but the living presence, the spirit of Harvester men, exists only as an echo of the past.

The routine of my job has led me frequently into the far corners of the world. It is one thing to manufacture the tools of agriculture; but if you do not yourself know how they are performing, you will lose touch. I have seen seventy-five-bushel wheat on a New Zealand farm and the machine-tearing roughness of the mallee district in Australia; tractors laboring in a Filipino jungle or marching over the endless rice terraces of Indo-China and Siam; motor trucks starting for the horizon of Manchuria or portering the burdens of New Japan. I have heard how fifty harvester-threshers in a line collect the yield of the Argentine pampas, how plows are redeeming the waste prairies of South Africa, and how power machinery is reviving the agriculture of Russia. The still-used reaper clatters through the small fields of Europe and Harvester implements perform the hardest labor of redeemed peasants.

In all these places I can feel at home. I can think of Alex Legge's story of a famous attorney called in to give counsel in a time of trouble. 'I have studied many corporations,' the lawyer said, 'but there is something in the Harvester Company deeper than in them all. You differ, you fight like cats and dogs for your opinions — but if you are attacked, you fight for each other. You are the best team I have ever seen. Why?'

Legge told him that this was due to the traditions of the inventor of the reaper and to the character of his son. He neglected to add that he himself had given his all to help my father instill Harvester Spirit in the International army. Together they brought about a square deal for all employees, a square deal for all customers. Perhaps, after all, loyalty to such an ideal is the Company's greatest single sales asset throughout the world.

CHAPTER XIV

THE HARVESTER SYSTEM OF PRODUCTION

THE production system of the International Harvester Company is not very different from that of other large, successful organizations. In origin it springs from the same circumstances that have made America the leading industrial nation in the world; and in development its growth has kept pace with the unfolding of our national commercial destiny. Industry has been America's leading contribution to modern civilization. We have produced great scholars, but none, it will be agreed, better than others in other parts of the world. We have produced great artists, but none to excel the sculptors, the painters, the musicians, and the architects of other climes. Our thinkers are noteworthy, but their abstractions can hardly rival those of the Orient. We are the most sizable free nation on the globe, but we did not invent democracy. We did, however, organize it more widely than any other people — because we approached it with the same mental vigor which has been able so broadly to organize our industry. We have offered our citizens the inspiring hope of politics for *all*, of education for *all* — and now, through our industrial system, we are exploring and claiming the first fruits of prosperity for *all*.

Our industrial development is the basis for our one claim to recognition in the eyes of the world. We have organized machinery and man-power, not merely as instruments of efficiency, but rather as the method of providing us with an ever-sufficient supply to meet our ever-increasing wants. The Nation has grown rich and materially powerful out of industry. Perhaps we feel that because we possess the things which other men cannot

gain with their unaided physical strength, we are not as
other men. We have a wage system that is admittedly
not yet perfect, but that gives workers the opportunity to
gain for themselves the best fruits of capitalism. We have
organized opportunity itself until it has been reduced to a
practical rule and is available for all men.

Possibly we who have so many advantages at our beck
and call do not sufficiently recognize that we have our
ancestors to thank for our present material prosperity.
They gave us our reapers, our railways, our electricity,
and the rudiments of our every instrument of production.
Of course we, with more experience and more sophistica-
tion than the pioneers could possibly possess, have improved upon the equipment they devised to satisfy their
lives. It is certainly as true of modern mechanics as of
modern science that if an individual had stopped learning
even in 1900 he would be hopelessly out-of-date to-day.
What of it? Our ancestors never ceased improving their
own work, and it is not too much to suppose that the
spirit of their genius is asking us to do likewise. They bequeathed to us the crude tools of their devising; and,
what is of far greater importance, they passed on to us the
inspiration of their achievement.

America is free politically and socially and intellectually, so free that we are never afraid to scrutinize our own
deeds with a criticism that compels us to go on and do
something better. American industry has developed out
of this attitude. Machinery, itself a product of the free
genius of liberated thought, rescued our national life
from the incubus of limitation and lifted industry to an
intellectual par with scholarship. It created wealth and a
steady supply of those rare comforts which we to-day
regard as essential. It created earning power which made
the acquisition of luxuries possible. Of course machinery

did not do this in an instant, since, like the inventive thought out of which it sprang, it was itself a progressive growth. So it has been with industry, at once the child and the parent of machinery. Industry is free-thinking, aggressive, self-expressive, and self-assertive; it is experiment-minded, in that it is ever willing to attempt the seemingly impossible; it is idealistic, in that it has been able to realize the dreams of other peoples; and, since it is so free from restricting limitations, it is representative of, and is the best product of, the free stream of American life.

It has been suggested elsewhere in this book that Cyrus Hall McCormick's influence was a vital force in the upbuilding of early American industry. We know that he was himself a pioneer in the origination of plans for distribution, credit to customers, advertising, and the like; and we may infer that the manufacturing methods employed in his factory were radically original and progressive. No adequate history of American industry had yet been written, and that part of it which deals with manufacturing is still sealed in the personal experience of the generation of men just passed or is the stock in trade of a younger generation, which even now is carving new experiences on the rocky cliffs of time. Therefore, as a prelude to a discussion of the production methods of the International Harvester Company, I shall take the liberty of stating what seem to me to be the fundamental principles of production's modern state:

Machinery is important only when interpreted in the light of its social importance to humanity. Thus, the reaper rendered man a double service by lightening his labor and increasing his supply of food.

Machinery is desirable only when it accomplishes

such tasks by producing more or better or cheaper articles than man, without its aid, can provide. Thus, transportation has made all the world neighbors and power has made man a king.

Machinery must fail if it be regarded as a substitute for brains. Its proper function is to serve man's individuality, not to master it. At the heart of industry lies the human equation.

There is no particular originality in this statement of the fundamental principles of machine production. They are modern and differ from the conception of the past in that, in harmony with the basic theories of American industry, they make machinery the servant of brains. They may be learned from factory managers and from factory workmen. The Harvester Company system, which may seem to a layman to be but designed to meet the necessity of the moment, is based on them. So also are they typical, perhaps not of all factories in the United States, but of the better ones. For all time, as long as men are men, there will be some who lead, some who follow. Because of the latter there will be conservatism, and because of the leaders there will be progress.

Eighty years ago the old McCormick shop by the Chicago River was an outstanding leader in the development of American manufacture. The inventor of the reaper did not himself plan this, but unquestionably he inspired it. Visitors came from afar to study manufacturing efficiency as exemplified by the processes in vogue in McCormick and Deering Works. In the middle period of Harvester history, every energy of his successors had to be given to selling. They fought successfully to hold their place, they expanded their business far beyond the realm he had bequeathed to them; and so it happened that their interest centered on the outward, dramatic elements of service to farmers rather than on stay-at-home matters of production.

It is not my present purpose to tell what the many factories of the International Harvester Company do. There are thirty-one of them and all are engaged in making the machines which are the latest generation of the reaper's progeny. Rather, I wish to suggest how and why they do their work, and also to relate how a change from an ancient to a modern scheme of production was brought about. Harvester's production is now as much in line as is its distribution with the aim of service to the farmer. All phases of the system are harmonized to bring about this one desired result, including the functions of designing, purchasing, manufacturing, and the other collateral activities which lend their strength to production.

It has already been suggested that the Harvester Company's rebirth into the realm of manufacturing efficiency was due partly to the cry for cost-reduction following the business depression of 1921 and partly to the tractor war which started in 1922. If I feel unable to assess the relative importance of these two causes, it is probably due to the fact that in those years the demand for lower production costs was so keen and so continually insistent that management had too little time for self-analysis. Suffice it to say that the post-war generation of Harvester factory men taught themselves a new efficiency.

Measured in terms of present knowledge — which is an admittedly unfair test — there was no such thing before 1915 as a really efficient manufacturing enterprise in the entire country. It is true that a few industries, such as the Chicago packing-houses, had accomplished marvels in the elimination of waste effort through the introduc-

tion of successively synchronized operations. But, because of comparatively low wages throughout the Nation, there was not the same urge as in recent years to
reduce labor cost by the elimination of labor waste.
There can be no proper control over the cost of production without the most careful scrutiny of the labor bill.
On the average, three-fourths of the cost of manufactured
articles represents labor devoted to it or to its constituent
materials. Even an electric generating station at the
mouth of a coal mine has to contemplate labor spent
in producing the metals for its transmission lines and in
erecting them before it can compute the labor content of
its product when in the hands of the consumer. In the
case of agricultural implements, where the most widely
used materials are pig iron, steel, and lumber, one must
consider the labor cost of these materials at the mines and
in the forests; the labor cost of transporting them to the
factory, not forgetting a share of the labor cost of building
the freight car which carried them; the labor cost of turning raw materials into a finished product; the labor cost of
distribution; and, since this is also the hardest kind of
labor, the human energy spent in organizing the ore from
the ground into the working tractor in the farmer's field.

Men did not realize these things as clearly as they do
now until the war-time demand for the production of
these supplies of all kinds, which Europe could no longer
make for itself, created a scarcity of labor. More men
were sought for the factories of the land than were available and, though women soon came forth to stand at the
bench beside their brothers and husbands, the shortage
resulted in a rapidly rising scale of wages. Early in 1917
the rising cost of labor began to be a matter of primary
concern. The automobile industry was still young at that
time. It had few precedents to stand as a bar to experi-

mentation and less of an investment in plant and equipment, so it was for the moment more easily able to as-
similate new doctrines than were the historic companies.
It made the startling discovery that there was an inherent difference between the price of labor and labor cost.
This was really no discovery at all, except to the adven-
turous young men of the automobile industry. Reaper
builders had known it of old, and so had makers of steel
and the designers of slaughter-houses. But the older generation had either forgotten what it had once discovered
for itself or had spent so much money developing its own
processes that it was content to rest on its laurels.

The automobile men found out that one could at the
same time reduce the labor content of a manufactured
article and leave the labor rate untouched. This they
were able to do by the provision of special manufacturing
equipment so designed that a machine tool would perform at once two or more operations on a piece. They
adopted exactly the same theory that, for example, had
underlain the development of mower-frame boring machines, and arranged to machine the different faces of a
crankcase at one pass through a milling machine. They
devised multiple drills and prepared types of speed
wrenches to enable a nut to be screwed more quickly on a
bolt. They sent men all over the world to bring back any
possible word of fast-working tools in other factories.
Most important of all, they organized crews of specialists
whose sole task was to study their own methods with a
view of simplification and improvement.

Some one of them discovered that, a few years before,
a mechanical engineer by the name of Frederick W. Taylor — who, more than any other man, is the father of
modern scientific manufacturing — had written a book to
prove that, when the successive operations of any produc-

tion program were planned in advance by the factory management rather than left to the discretion of an individual foreman, time could be saved. Taylor showed, for example, that without additional strain a workman could lift more weight if he were instructed how best to bend over and how to use his muscles. Out of this simple illustration has arisen the vast store of scientific time and motion study which is now applied in every efficient factory. Out of it, also, has come the practice of bringing the work to the man rather than the man to the work; and that most spectacular, but by no means the most crucial, accomplishment of factory efficiency, the conveying of materials by mechanism rather than by hand. The now-familiar assembly chains of automotive and other factories are a development of the same theory. It is this ordered succession of machining operations, properly called 'processed' manufacturing, but popularly known as 'progressive machining,' which, introduced after 'progressive assembly,' has become the foundation of the most modern methods of mass production.

During the early years when modern efficiency was being introduced into manufacturing, it is possible that the automobile world as a whole was no more than searching out the road to its present advanced state in an effort to counteract the rising cost of labor, but the fact that it was seeking was something. Between 1917 and 1922 it made giant strides of advance. Such Harvester men as were engaged in the production of tractors and motor trucks were in closer touch with the new methods than were the implement builders. They were constructing an automotive product and were already seeking to adopt automotive methods. The motor-car factories were making no secret of their success in reducing labor cost through labor elimination. Secretary of Commerce Herbert Hoover was urging American industry to save for itself and for the public the terrific cost of wasteful methods. The severe lessons of the extravagant post-war years and of the 1921 depression, which forced business men to save or fall, were fresh in the minds of all. The public had long been intrigued by Henry Ford's successive announcements of prices lowered in proportion to rising volume. The time was ripe for the Harvester Company to resume its ancient supremacy in the methods of early mass production.

The two tractor plants, Milwaukee Works and Tractor Works, were even then the most mechanically efficient of the Company's factories. The production cost of the old twin-cylinder tractor, the Titan 10–20, had long been surprisingly low; and when the new McCormick-Deering 15–30 was introduced in 1922, every known labor-saving device was provided for its production. When the 10–20, a smaller companion, was brought into being at Tractor Works a few months later, even greater strides in efficient manufacture were made. Most of the departments there were on a single floor level, so the possibilities for progressive methods were greater than at Milwaukee, which was a reconstructed implement factory of the older multiple-story type. It is perhaps a noteworthy tribute to the plans then put into effect that the sale price of these two tractors works out at less than nineteen cents per pound of weight as compared to twenty-two cents in the case of the cheapest automobiles in existence.

I do not wish to convey the impression that nothing except the necessities of the depression and the tractor war could ever have driven the Harvester Company into improved manufacturing efficiency. As early as 1919, the men of its automotive factories gave over their formerly self-contained habits and traveled ceaselessly through other plants to learn what the rest of the manufacturing world was doing. They were by no means oblivious to the developing progress of the automobile industry, but did not have such large production schedules with which to deal. Harvester engineers, too, were experiencing the benefits of contact with automotive standards, as witness the outstandingly original design of the two new tractors. It is true, however, that the Company's manufacturing staff arrived more quickly at the desired goal because of the pressure of necessity. The same cause was also instructive to the higher management.

Industry is a living, progressing thing. In the days of the construction of McCormick Works — and of the first automobile factories too, for that matter — it did not occur to industrial architects not to put up multiple-story buildings. It began at length to be apparent that a single-story building, with its floor space spread out on one level, would permit a simpler, and therefore more efficient, development of operations. Thus, Harvester's new motor-truck plant at Fort Wayne, designed in 1920, is principally one-story; but the production arrangements planned at that time have since been radically improved as the science of production planning has advanced.

The same modern manufacturing methods which were worked out in the Company's automotive factories between 1919 and 1923 have in recent years been applied as far as practicable to the older agricultural implement works. The implement factories have all been completely reconditioned in the last five years. When progressive operations were introduced into McCormick Works, for example, all the departments were rearranged, every piece of machinery in the plant was relocated, and in the end the same manufacturing capacity was secured from half the former floor area. Thus, without additional buildings, the plant was able to take care of its share of the greatly enlarged requirements for farm equipment occasioned by the enlarged demands of modern times. A member of the old staff at Springfield or Canton would hardly recognize his former work home in the close-pressed maze of machine tools and conveying equipment which the new arrangement permits the ancient walls to house. At Hamilton, two separate factories have been consolidated into one, and a complete twine mill, re-moved from Deering, has been installed in a former plow works. Deering itself, in its product at least, has been changed beyond recognition and to-day houses that most modern of all farm implements, the harvester-thresher.

Thus the many Harvester Company factories have first caught up with, and then kept abreast of, modern times. It is not claimed that an old, reconditioned multiple-story plant can be made as efficient as a new, scientifically designed one-story installation. But Harvester's experience has proved to its own satisfaction that, given modern methods, a complete abandonment of out-worn practices, a 'processed' arrangement of machinery, suitable material-handling systems, adequate lighting and ventilating, and above all a personnel trained and aggressive and willing to learn, an old factory can be made efficient enough to avoid the overhead charge for new construction.

In all of the factories there is as highly developed a system of mass production as the volume of product will permit. Quite obviously an implement for which there is a trade demand of five thousand a year cannot carry the burden of special manufacturing equipment, assembly chains, and the like which can desirably be supported by a production of a hundred thousand units. Harvester makes no one article of which as many are sold as the cheaper motor cars. If the Company's manufacturing methods are now as efficient as those of the automobile world, it is because it has never refused to provide the factories with labor-saving, cost-reducing, quality-improving machinery.

Machinery is the essential of mass production. The successive machining and assembly operations from the basic raw material to the finished product must be studied in advance and so related one to another that neither time nor effort is wasted between or during operations. Materials must be conveyed to and from a machine tool so that the operator may conserve his energy for direction. Equipment performs the heavy labor, the workman does the thinking. He has a brain which it cannot rival and it has an untiring physique which he cannot match. Together they are unbeatable — but always the process is the servant of the man.

Mass production permits a company executive to plan his business campaign in advance, sure in the knowledge that, once he has provided the factory with an estimate of requirements, the nicely balanced succession of operations will start to function and will provide him with what he wants at the time he wants it. The cost of production will be lower than by the time-honored, hit-or-miss methods of production, for waste will have been eliminated, and machines, while they will wear out if unattended, will not tire. Man will do the thinking for them, and, if he be watchful, will see that cutters do not dull or fixtures become displaced. Thus, mass production and its constant appeal to brains emphasizes thought and so becomes an instrument for answering the world's increasing demand for quality. It is perhaps significant that the best quality implements are those which are produced in the greatest numbers by the most completely progressive methods. And the farmer in a faraway corner of the world who needs a repair part for his mower or his motor truck will find that, because of standardization, its dimensions are exactly the same as his old part. He puts it on and proceeds with his task.

Any such integrated system of manufacture puts a strain not merely on the factories. What would happen if, in the middle of a smoothly flowing mass-production program, it were suddenly discovered that the purchasing agent had failed to provide pig iron and the foundry could not make castings in time for the machine shop to function? Or if a traffic man had failed to secure freight cars for the day of shipment? Or if a construction engineer was unable to complete a new building when it was needed? Or if a designing engineer could not finish his experimental work on a new part early enough to permit all these other portions of the whole grand scheme of production to function in time to deliver the desired implements to their future owners? In truth, the ramified problems of mass production are many and the system of management which can solve them is worthy. This, American industry has done.

How much good there has been in all of this, time can tell better than the generation that has done the job. Harvester men are not perfect, but on the whole the Company has been reasonably successful in its production efforts. Much money has been spent on capital improvements. Production costs have been kept under control in the face of high labor rates, quality has been improved, manufacturing schedules have been maintained, and the demands of farmers for an ever-increasing supply of labor-saving, food-producing equipment have been met. The entire scheme of production has been rebuilt — or, perhaps, it is fairer to say that it is being rebuilt, for to keep pace with the ebb and flow of business means an ever-unrolling series of improvements. Two factories have been entirely abandoned, due to new conditions, three have been completely changed from one line of manufacture to another, four new ones have been started. Production has been integrated so that now three different tractor models consume the energies of three factories; twine is spun in three places, depending on distribution; implements are made in seven different factories according to their type, and three plants are devoted to the production of collateral parts. There is a complete steel-making installation with supporting ore and coal mines. The various foreign affiliated companies operate ten factories in Canada, France, Germany, and Sweden.

It has been my own personal pleasure to know that they have one and all of them become reasonably efficient. Only a few years ago Harvester plant superintendents and foremen used to visit the motor centers to learn how the outside world conducted its production enterprises. They still travel in search of information, for when men stop learning, they stop growing; and it is certainly true of modern factories that an open-door policy toward visitors gains more than it loses. But the tide has turned, and the Harvester plants are now receiving visitors, even from Detroit, come to learn how manufacturing should be organized. There was a time when potential buyers of motor trucks for city use, who knew nothing of farm demands for quality, used to question Harvester's ability to manufacture up to automotive standards. But times have changed, and the production of the instruments of power farming demands the best manufacturing skill in the world. The former 'old implement company' whose methods were once scorned by the youthful proponents of the automobile, which was thought to understand nothing except cast iron or lumber, and to which such niceties as fine manufacturing limits and the heat treatment of alloy steels were supposed to be a closed book, has changed. It has become young and aggressive again. The efficiency of its manufacturing methods is second to none.

If one should seek to scrutinize the Harvester production system, or indeed any other in the field of American industry, to discover its most important element, it is probable that management would finally be chosen. But this is no more than another way of saying that the most important element in business — in life itself — is the human factor. Business cannot be successful unless its personnel be sound; and if the president of a company at the top or common labor at the bottom be not sound, that organization will fail. Harvester is actuated by ideals which are great and traditional, but ideals fade if they are not given life and reality in the hands of men. It is fortunate for the Company that the present application of Cyrus Hall McCormick's conception of justice and of Cyrus H. McCormick's reiterated demand for fair play has succeeded in providing a happy relationship between it and its forty thousand factory workers.

The story of the Harvester Company's early excursion into the field of welfare has been told. In 1908, when an aggressive interest in the human problem was evinced, the things the Company did to establish pensions, benefit insurance, factory safety, first aid, employee stock ownership, and the like were a very radical departure from the usual practice of employers. In the intervening years, every action then taken has been proved to be sound and has been enlarged. During the course of its history, International has paid out $7,000,000 for pensions and has established a pension trust of $23,000,000 to protect the old age of its faithful employees. To insure the future integrity of pension funds, the trust has been made irrevocable. The Employees' Benefit Association, maintained by employee subscriptions and Company contributions, has spent nine and a half million dollars to the end of 1929 in sickness and death benefits. The record for safety through the years is the best of any large company in the country. The first-aid stations have become organized hospitals, each in charge of capable medical authorities. Employee stock ownership has progressed at such a pace that between 1908 and 1929 no less than 800,000 shares of stock were sold to employees of all ranks, and the end is not yet. A new stock plan was announced in the spring of 1930, and the indications are that many more shares will be bought by employees on the favorable terms offered. In 1929, a highly successful plan of vacations with pay for wage-earning employees was put into effect.

In March, 1919, there occurred an event which for all time stamped the International Harvester Company as one of the most forward-looking of industrial organizations — the adoption of the Harvester Industrial Council Plan. This plan provided for a works council at each plant, composed of representatives elected by the factory employees in proportion to their number and of nominees appointed by the management. The council was to discuss and take action upon anything which affected the well-being of the workmen, including such possibly controversial matters as wages, hours, and working conditions. Neither the management side nor the elected representatives could outvote the other, but an appeal to the president of the Company or to arbitrators was provided in case of a deadlock. True to its traditional open-shop principles, the Company published an absolute guaranty in the plan of no discrimination against any employee because of race, sex, political or religious affiliation, or membership in any labor or other organization.

This is the frame of the Magna Charta of Harvester workmen. At first some of them regarded it suspiciously, fearing that such an apparently munificent gift from an employer must have some strings tied to it somewhere. When they were called upon to vote whether or not they would accept its terms and do business under them, most of them agreed to give the plan a trial, but the men of McCormick Works, largest of the factories, would have none of it. Some of the manufacturing executives were also opposed to its terms. They were hurt that the officials of the Company had not consulted them in preparing such a radical departure in labor policy, they did not understand it, they feared it would affect their ability to maintain discipline, and certain of the older men were constitutionally opposed to any compromise with labor. The Company's higher executives believed sincerely in this forward step in industrial relations; but they feared that premature discussion would crystallize both ultra-conservative and ultra-radical opposition. Hence the works councils were started quietly. As a matter of fact, this speed almost defeated the purpose.

In subsequent years a better way of introducing such a plan was found. Like political democracy, an industrial bill of rights must be understood in order to be appreciated. It was not strange that foremen who had grown up in the old, outworn school of direct-action factory management did not understand that a modern world which was using modern machinery would also require a modern attitude toward labor problems. They did not appreciate the fact that the guaranty of good faith to workmen was also inferentially a guaranty of fair and adequate management, which necessarily involves the maintenance of plant discipline. Neither they nor the first employee representatives grasped the analogy that, just as good citizens support the police powers of an organized community, so it is to the interests of the better workmen in a factory to support the management.

Any business enterprise is an oligarchy insofar as a few men must manage. The test of ability to direct industry is brains. Industry must seek out brains wherever it can find them and endow them with power. Add an inherent belief in the doctrine of fair play and you have a complete picture of the proper interrelation between factory management and a works council. Workmen do not wish to manage production, since they know that their superior officers, mostly men who have risen from the ranks, have climbed because of superior ability. But wage-earners are interested in their own well-being, in the wages they receive and the hours they work. They do not like to read on their department bulletin board a cold notice announcing baldly the termination of employment and never have a chance to learn the reason. After all, would you?

During the first several meetings of each one of the Harvester works councils there was much hesitation and friction. Management appointees who did not understand the scheme were willing to give lip service to the plan because the Company wished it. Employee representatives were feeling out the sincerity of the Company and trying to discover what new rights they could win for their constituents. Much time was spent in stubborn contention about complaints, some of them fancied, some of them real. But on both sides were many serious men who, catching in the works council plan a glimpse of the future, were trying to grope their way toward mutual benefits to be gained for all from better industrial relations. They persevered and they have won out.

A works council meeting now, after the years of experience and mutual growth, is no routine event, though its business is more expeditiously transacted. There are no appeals to the president of the Company to settle deadlocks, nor are there many debates on complaints to adjudicate. The employee representative has already taken up his constituent's case with his foreman or, in want of satisfaction there, with the plant superintendent. Reasonable men find it easy to reach reasonable and quick decisions. The representative merely reports to the council that such and such a decision has been agreed upon. He has learned that the management is sincere and that the spoken word of a Harvester man is a contract. The foreman, also, and perhaps even the superintendent, has been promoted to his present position, probably from the ranks, since the introduction of the council plan. He has never done business in the old-fashioned way, or known the times when the interests of management and men were theoretically hostile. It is as natural for him to discuss Bill's grievances or Tom's unexplained absence with an employee representative as it used to be to curse a stock chaser for failure to provide material.

The foreman and the representative are much more interested in what they call 'constructive policies' than they are in grievances — of which, due partly to modern, fair thinking about labor problems and partly to the influence of the fact of works councils, there are now so few. The vacation plan for wage-earners came out of the councils, the various stock subscription plans were formulated with their assistance, and they have been the medium through which the men have learned much about the economics of the business. Thus, in the dreary days of the depression of 1921, they were brought to understand the necessity of reducing wages, just as in other circumstances they have also been instrumental in persuading the management to see the necessity of wage increases. Most difficult of all, employee representatives have been able to learn from certain council meetings why changing business conditions would compel the Company to close for all time the factory where they had worked for many years. In the three cases of this kind, the management and the elected representatives of the men have collaborated to find new jobs for *all* of the employees. I admit that such a method, new and helpful though it may be, does not entirely solve the problem of a workman's ever-present fear of losing his job; but at least it is better than the former plan of posting a brusque notice that work would stop with the end of the current day.

The Industrial Relations Department was organized at the time works councils were introduced to father them, to centralize and standardize employment methods, and to represent the interest of the workers. It is now a separate institution in theory only; for the management of labor has become an integral part of the production system. Harvester superintendents and foremen are human enough to understand that workmen are not machines, but are reasoning beings like themselves. As a matter of fact, any one who thinks otherwise is missing the best chance in life of a friendly association. Any one who believes that none of the errors arising out of the surging rush of production can be charged to the superintendent of a factory fails miserably to secure the support and assistance of that wise individual, the American workman. So it is that works councils are able, if they believe in the management, to accomplish many other things: safety, for example, the scientific setting of wage rates, and the high quality of workmanship that comes from understanding, not from orders.

Harvester factories have always been safe places to

work and their record before the inception of works councils was highly satisfactory. It had been achieved by enormous pressure from the top. Machine tools were guarded and statistics indicated that the vast majority of accidents were due to 'employee negligence.' Then the representatives took hold of the problem. A workman can explain to a workman so much better than a foreman can why, for his own sake, he must play safe. However good the International Harvester Company's record for safety may have been, it improved remarkably as soon as the elected representatives were enlisted in the cause. Quite incidentally it is estimated that their influence has resulted in a direct wage saving of $3.28 a year for every workman on the pay roll.

The interest of the works council representatives in the system of so-called 'occupational rating,' an elaborate general job specification that classified the relative value of different factory occupations, and in time-study and other scientific methods of rate setting, has been part and parcel of their growing and intelligent interest in the broad system of manufacturing efficiency. Ten years ago one would not have dared expose a time-study stop-watch for fear of arousing opposition; or its presence would have been a silent signal for a workman to slow down his pace in order, as he thought, to get a higher rate. Now, because through the intervention of their own representatives they understand the scientific and wholesome nature of such things, workmen welcome the time-study man. They know he represents the efficiency department and that efficiently organized production means not only savings for the Company but higher earnings for the men. Labor elimination means fewer men; but, unless times are bad, the doctrine of high wages brings high consuming power into being, and that in turn carries with it jobs for all. Labor-saving devices mean faster production, but they also mean less grueling work for a man's muscles, better working conditions and more pay.

Another constructive policy much discussed at works council meetings is the question of quality. Here the direct benefits to workmen are more remote. Except as a means to avoid the usual 'charge back' for spoiled work, quality's one appeal is for an interest in the ultimate customer. It has been surprising to find how many workmen are ex-farmers and know the requirements of the field. It has also been surprising to find how many other workmen had been producing some particular piece for years and yet did not know how it functioned or why it had to be made just so. To-day there are show rooms in every Harvester factory where an employee may study his own work in place upon a complete machine. Alex Legge said, 'Quality is the foundation of our business.' The answer to this challenge is perhaps to be found in the vital interest the works council members have taken for the past several years in the subject. The representatives have learned how to show their constituents the way to an intelligent interest in their jobs — the quality way, the way of building better machines for better farmers.

Under the former most excellent system of welfare work, which could more correctly have been called 'industrial betterment,' the many desirable schemes put into effect were imposed from the top. A wise management did those things which it knew were good for workmen. Under the modern system of industrial relations, workmen have an opportunity to do their own thinking. That, it seems to me, is the fundamental difference between the two. It is this that employee representatives are striving for when they preach quality in no uncertain tones. They are not becoming the agents of management. Rather, they are trying to help the great body of workmen to better themselves, to become individuals who will have pride in their jobs — to become better citizens of the world of industry.

At the risk of invidious comparison between factories, I mention two concrete illustrations. The McCormick works council — the men of this plant petitioned the Company to install the council plan when they heard how well it was operating in the other factories — telegraphed me proudly not so long ago that the third successive month had passed without a major error of manufacturing quality. Six thousand men at work, and yet the inspectors could not find one serious variance from specifications! Recently, also, I had a talk with the men of the mower department and congratulated them on building 250,000 mowers on the new progressive assembly chain without one single complaint from the field. Is it strange that I believe that the modern production system, both as concerns equipment methods and the administration of personnel, breeds quality, or that I feel that Harvester workmen have come to take pride in their work? Is it any wonder that I have learned to stand solidly for works councils and that I believe that in their sincerity lies the solution of all industrial relations problems?

Experience with the Harvester system of production has convinced me, first, that the matter of personnel is the most crucial subject with which a manufacturer has to deal, and, second, that an executive in a large American company need look no further than his own ranks for material for the personnel of the future. It is his particular task to find and train these men. This is easy if he searches aggressively, for Americans take naturally to instruction and are all of them potential organizers. Not every workman can rise to the top, but when one of them does rise it spurs others on to emulation. It makes little difference whether a candidate for promotion is a college man come to the manufacturing world to win his way or a graduate of the workbench. But he must have brains; and he must have courage to stand the competition for preferment. It will serve him if he has shown the ability to climb up through the ranks. Whoever and whatever he may be, the essentially democratic manufacturing world will accept him if he can produce. Factory work demands men who do things and it has small patience either with the machine or the individual that fails. It likes to give a newcomer a chance and to instruct him. But once he has become a part of the system, he must win out or fall. If he wants to rise, all he has to do is prove his ability to make good in competition with other able men who are striving for promotion.

The opportunity to win promotion is, I think, the greatest single factor in the American industrial system. We are even less in danger of being caste-ridden in our commerce than in our social life. We offer rewards to those who can prove that they have the brains to claim them. There is no part of industry where the competition of man against man is keener or more able than in the field of production. In the case of the Harvester Company manufacturing and raw material properties there are eleven general supervisory positions and thirty superintendencies. Of the former, only one man fills the same position he held ten years ago and one exercises similar but broader responsibilities. Of the other nine, five were not even factory superintendents a decade ago. Out of the thirty superintendents, five hold the jobs they had ten years ago and four others were heads of less important plants. The manufacturing game demands that men grow quickly.

HEAT TREATING DEPARTMENT OF THE INTERNATIONAL
MOTOR-TRUCK WORKS, FORT WAYNE, INDIANA

FRONT YARD OF THE McCORMICK WORKS, CHICAGO

CHAPTER XV

ADMINISTRATION OF THE HARVESTER COMPANY

IT IS remarkable that during the century of the reaper, the hundred-year period that includes within its limits the tale of such stirring, man-made events and also the record of such increasing service to agriculture, so few men have guided this vehicle of achievement. Cyrus Hall McCormick initiated progress and then himself carried it on until beyond its fiftieth anniversary. His son, Cyrus, bred in his tradition and trained under his direction, carried his work through the stormy middle period when able competitors sought to win away from the second generation what the old lion, the founder of the business, had established. Nettie F. McCormick, wife and mother of these leaders, provided the link of continuity between the generations and, because she was as able as any president, might well have held their place. Then came the International Harvester Company, and the circumstance of his own work held Cyrus H. McCormick, still young and inspired by the deeds of the past and the hope of the future, in the leadership. This he retained through all the troubled years of pioneer organization, litigation, and war until, in 1918, he turned a secure and enlarged business over to his brother, Harold.

It is a cardinal principle of growth that each successor must add something to the equipment he has received from his predecessors. Without this there would be no development, no progress, but only decay and the slow crumbling of achievement that ends in oblivion. Thus, Cyrus H. McCormick enlarged upon his father's definition of implacable justice by extending it to the limitless term, fair play; and he softened an inherited determination with a restraint and a willingness to compromise which won him many battles wherein refusal to admit the validity of an opposing point of view would have resulted in stalemate. Perhaps the latter of these qualities is really an outgrowth of the former; and certainly it was his unequivocal fairness — his example of truth to all men and in all situations — which is the living root of Harvester Spirit.

It is probable that no one with less tolerance, less perseverance, and less ability could have continued the work of Cyrus Hall McCormick, enlarged the world-wide scope of the McCormick Harvesting Machine Company, and led the International Harvester Company through the precarious but glowing years of its youth. It was left for Harold, born of one leader and trained by another, to be the third pilot on the broad seas of the reaper's destiny, to endow the whole organization with the fruits of the most winning of all personalities. He crowned the fine structure of Harvester Spirit and made the lowest or the highest conscious of a bond of ready, personal affection linking Harvester men together, not so much as a team ready for the game as in a brotherhood. A 'soul-less' corporation may be endowed with character if the personality of its commander permits. Under their second president, Harvester men learned more than ever before that one of the chief duties of a subordinate is to express himself fearlessly about organization policies; and thus they carried still further the development of a business character.

Then, in 1922, came Legge, the McCormick-trained product of the Harvester ranks. He had learned to plan when he rode alone over the Western plains, he had learned determination as he fought his way upward in the harsh days of the harvester war, he had learned how to judge men in his contact with humanity. Farm-bred and farm-wise, he understood farm problems as few others. Courageous, far-seeing, able, a fighter, kind or severe as the case deserved, worthy of respect and admiration, every inch a leader whom men leaped to follow, Alex Legge has been a captain whom men loved and respected, though he might oppose them, and clamored for places under his leadership because he never failed them. He and the masters who preceded him were men of understanding and ideals. An organization, no matter how good the men who make up the rank and file, is no better than its leader. His men take him for their inspiration, they model their conduct on his character, they look to him for the challenge which the ability to lead always inspires.

The internal administration of the International Harvester Company is not inherently different from that of other large corporations. There is, under the president, an executive council composed of the nine chief officers. They are at the same time representatives in the council deliberations of their own special interests and arbiters of general company policy. Their discussion brings possibly conflicting, certainly individualistic opinion to bear on all matters which, as most do, touch interests other than those of a single department. It might surprise an outsider to hear the controversies that take place around the council table; but, since the strength of unanimity is in action resulting from deliberation, such of the foundation of farm implement progress as is laid there is sure.

Plans are criticized there and strengthened, but the ideas on which they are based frequently come from below. Some people say that the mental power of an executive can be measured in terms of the ability of his juniors to think. The chief usually has more experience than the subordinate, and is able, therefore, to spur him on to aggressive mental energy and at the same time act as a proper check on youthful enthusiasm. Such, at all events, is the way of the Harvester Company. The juniors in the departments know that their suggestions will be considered and so put up plan after plan for discussion, a department head studies them, and then the executive council deliberates, criticizes, amends, and takes action. When the whole cycle is complete, the scheme, if adopted, will in all probability contain less risk as well as more potential progress.

The main departments which direct the Company's activities are: executive, treasury, accounting, law, and agricultural extension; sales, stock, collections, and advertising; manufacturing, industrial relations, engineering, and purchasing; and steel, fiber, traffic, patents, and construction. I have deliberately refrained from listing them as they are grouped under the members of the executive council because it is a cardinal element of Harvester policy that there shall be no restricting or constricting organization chart. The Company's activities are thought of in terms of their object. To meet the constantly changing demands of farm life, the framework must be flexible. Also, a business group is after all nothing more than a collection of men, some of whom are strong and can carry much responsibility, some of whom are weak if they are overloaded and yet entirely adequate within a limited sphere. Therefore, the head of the organization should at all times be able to swing an activity from one department to another, depending upon the men available to carry the load.

Again I say that the training of men is the chief job of any executive. Whether he is high or low, he cannot be said to be fulfilling the responsibilities placed upon him unless he is able at any moment to nominate his own successor. He is the friend and the impartial judge of all of the men under him. He fights their battles against the world, and at the same time creates competition for promotion so that, when it comes time to make a choice among them, the successful candidate will be a better man because he has been pressed ahead by a close rival. He keeps the narrowing funnel of candidates for promotion full by feeding new ones in at the bottom. Some men will thrust their heads above any crowd, but such rare individuals are few; and yet with a little training many will prove that they have potential brains which, when developed, will each have a contribution to make to the whole. By the same token he is prepared, hard though it may seem, to weed out weak men in order to make room for strong ones. One of the wisest of all Harvester men once said to me, 'It is no sin to make a mistake and pick the wrong man for a job, but it is a crime to leave him there after you know he is the wrong man.' Workmen realize at least as soon as the factory superintendent when their foreman is weak; and a man's associates are as aware of his faults as of his strength. The executive gains no respect in the minds of his subordinates if he temporizes in matters of personnel. For the building of organization morale, the art of dismissing inferior men is second only to the art of promoting good ones.

Always there are men in the lower operating positions in training for future enlarged responsibilities. Experience is the fundamental of correct practice. Executive control requires knowledge of what is happening on the firing line. As a matter of fact the policy of traveling abroad to study the field operation of Harvester-made machinery has from time immemorial been an element of the executive control of the farm implement business. No written report can possibly convey as eloquent a message as one look at a tractor binder struggling in Alberta wheat, no letter would ever be able to tell adequately the story of cotton cultivation in Texas. Farm problems seem to vary with the wind. One must go to them, study them, let them explain themselves, before one can have any true comprehension of agriculture or agricultural implements. The engineers and the factory men have learned to realize that a plow built for sandy soil will too often meet stones, the salesmen have come to understand production conditions and so are able to sell and service production-made machinery. Most of all, Harvester executives travel abroad and get their information at first hand from the field. They have gained much inspiration from the men on the firing line and have brought to the far frontiers whatever help there may be in the contact of field and factory with the parent source of Harvester Spirit.

One of the subdivisions of the Company's activities listed above is the Agricultural Extension Department. No account of the century following the invention of the reaper would be complete without a reference to it; and yet, due to the circumstances surrounding its origin and organization, it is impossible to discuss it in the same breath with any of International's commercial achievements. At about the time when the International Harvester Company was first venturing into the field of welfare work for its employees, it occurred to Cyrus H. McCormick that the Company might properly interest itself in the general welfare of its chosen public, the farmers. Accordingly a small service bureau was organized which distributed bulletins and the like giving advice on general farm problems. These bulletins dealt, not with any phase of Harvester's business, but rather with the day-to-day problems arising out of farm operation. So well were they received throughout the agricultural community that it soon became necessary to enlarge the scope of the work, and in 1912 a separate department was organized.

The Agricultural Extension Department has no connection with any of the Harvester Company's other departments. It is wholly non-commercial. Its entire business is to demonstrate and popularize good farming methods, not farm machinery. It is an educational institution akin to a State agricultural college, though, being both private and nation-wide, it can attack any farm problem anywhere. It is a service bureau for farmers which seeks to increase farm production and reduce farm waste; to improve rural living conditions; to make the farmer more prosperous; to help him safeguard his family's health; to advise his wife how her housework may be made easier and her life happier; and to instill into the minds of farm boys and girls an enduring love for the farm and a greater interest in the pursuit of agriculture.

Consistent with these objects, Harvester's president is reported to have said, 'I believe that every company or organization of men doing business in any community, no matter where or how removed from the central office, is in duty bound to do something to help build that community, aside from the things required by law or the things beneficial to itself. The Harvester Company is a citizen of every community in which it sells a machine, and it is not a good citizen if it does not perform some service in that community, the same as any citizen who lives there would be expected to perform.'

To accomplish its service functions, the Agricultural Extension Department maintains a staff of agricultural experts, several of them drawn from the faculties of agricultural colleges. It provides crews of speakers and demonstrators who conduct short courses or more extensive campaigns on agricultural or home problems. It furnishes lecturers who participate in educational or other community gatherings and speak on agricultural subjects. It has prepared a great number of charts, lantern slides, and motion-picture films, which are lent to county agents, farmers' organizations, schools, and chambers of commerce for use in their work, or even to an individual who exhibits a sincere desire to labor in his community for the cause of agricultural betterment. It has published a variety of booklets dealing with modern methods of dairying, cropping, poultry, organizing farm housework, and kindred subjects. It maintains one of the best libraries on agricultural subjects in the country, and corresponds with countless individual farmers who write to ask advice on this or that particular problem. Since the department was organized, members of the staff have spoken at 23,600 meetings to more than four and a half million people. Seventeen million booklets have been sold at cost and its articles have been reprinted in thousands of publications. A million people a year see its charts and films in the hands of other lecturers.

An important function of the Agricultural Extension Department is the operation of several demonstration farms. These are situated principally in the Southeastern States, in the Northwest, and in Canada, where adverse climatic or soil or other conditions make the perplexities of farm life keener. These farms are not equipped with anything not usable by, or beyond the reach of, an average farmer in the community. The farms are chosen with a view of proving to local agriculturists that they can profitably work the land in their own district. In the South, the Department's practical scientists have shown how run-down cotton plantations may be redeemed and devoted to dairy and diversified farming. In the North-west, propaganda has been spread for soil conservation and the raising of corn and cattle. Everywhere the demonstration farms have taught the all-important message of diversification, agriculture's insurance against the perils of one-crop farming.

It is obvious that work of this kind is well-nigh as important to the well-being of farmers as is that of the State agricultural colleges. Indeed, there is the closest coöperation between them and the department. In each case the object is precisely similar: farm prosperity. It may be objected that, in maintaining an extension department, the International Harvester Company is really doing a selfish work. To be sure, the Company is laboring to make farmers prosperous; and, since they are its principal customers, it is to be presumed that prosperity for them will mean a greater sale of its machines. One might as well suggest that the States maintain agricultural colleges in order to increase the taxable assets of their citizens. But Harvester is more interested in aiding the welfare of farmers than in proving the impersonal nature of its attitude toward extension work. The farmers of the country know that it is sincere. The Company knows that it can have no success in business unless farming is profitable.

The Harvester Company's business is by no means outstandingly profitable. But it is a fine business. It deals with farming, the most basic of all industries. Its products are essential to farm production and prosperity. It has service to render as well as goods to sell. It is no wonder that Harvester men speak of their organization, not as 'International,' but as 'Harvester.' There is real pride as they let the name roll over their lips, real gratitude as they think of the satisfaction they have earned. They are loyal, they have ideals, they serve. Perhaps, even to-day, in all the hurly-burly of modern life and modern business, some of them feel as does that old pensioner whose wife remarked the other day: 'Yes, my man always was a good carpenter. I used to beg and plead with him for years to get away from the shop and be a contractor and builder. He could have made a lot more money to raise six children on. But no, he was so in love with that old corn husker of his that he just wouldn't leave it.'

CHAPTER XVI

THE INDUSTRY OF THE FUTURE

THE scope of the farm implement industry of the future, considered either in terms of its own success or of its ability to keep abreast of agriculture, will depend entirely on how farmers solve the problems which are now, and for several years past have been, giving them concern. Prosperity is one matter; the handling of prosperity is another. It would take a bolder prophet than I to suggest the successive steps to be taken on the road to prosperity, but the way itself is reasonably clear. A part of this way has lain within the chosen province of International Harvester and its constituent units. Throughout the years of the reaper century, they sought as they could and in their own field to foster farm prosperity.

In the long run the industry of farming cannot but be profitable. The population of the world is increasing and the quantity of land is fixed. Men must eat. Such difficulty as there is lies in the short swing. The farm problem is complicated by the fact that it is social as well as economic. There are six million and more farms in the United States, counting truck gardens as well as hundred-thousand-acre wheat factories. These farms are occupied by a fifth of the Nation's population. But a hundred years ago three-quarters of our people lived by agriculture. Even so, the increasing population of the country has continued to be fed and clothed with the products of the declining number who have remained on the land, and much has been left over for export. This, it seems, is a correct measure of the whole-hearted effort which the farmer has invested in his own individual efficiency.

The National Census gave no figures with regard to occupations until 1850. Since that time the number of persons gainfully employed in agriculture has doubled. But the number engaged in all occupations has increased six times. There are ten times as many employees in the Nation's factories, and the staff of its transportation system is thirty times as great as it was. The value of all American produce has increased much more than the ratio of one to six because of the individual and collective efficiency which the United States offers as its best contribution to civilization. The ten times as many industrial workers eat better food than before and the army of thirty times the previous number of transportation employees is better clothed. The increasing wants of the greatly increased numbers have been supplied by only double the number of farmers.

The above ratios indicate that the farmer has kept fair pace with the rate of urban efficiency. In actual numbers those persons gainfully employed in agriculture (which total neglects children, the hope of the future, and those superannuated men and women whose work lies behind them) are even now actually decreasing. In 1900 the figure stood at less than 10,900,000, whereas in 1929 it is estimated at 10,400,000. That is what the rapid development of farm equipment has enabled farmers to do. With every possible aid of machinery and the telling methods of mass production, the factory worker has increased his annual output forty-four per cent since 1900, according to the National Industrial Conference Board. During the same time the farmer has increased his production forty-seven per cent. He has done so principally because he has provided himself with modern equipment. With machinery — and it was good machinery, as far as it went — but without any collective action, the advancing efficiency of the farm has equaled the improvement in industry, aided though it was by mass production.

In these same years there has occurred a tremendous growth of the export trade in manufactured articles. This has been accomplished without disturbing the constant advance of what is known as the American standard of living. Efficiency has allowed American production, either because of superior quality or because of a lower price, to overcome the apparent initial advantage of a lower European rate of wages and the Oriental problem of a superfluity of numbers. But we have seen fit to protect our standard of living by a high protective tariff wall, which has availed little in the case of agriculture because we are exporters and not even potential importers of the principal farm products. I do not seek to discuss what is manifestly a controversial politico-economic question, but it appears obvious that the answer to the farm problem lies, as it lay in the case of industry, in a further reduction of the cost of production to enable American farmers to compete for the world markets. Farmers as a group have already invested themselves with unexcelled efficiency. Yet their trade is languishing because they have been unable to protect their standard of living in comparison with that of the cities.

There is much real hope for the future in the possibility of lower farm production costs. Consider only what the harvester-thresher has done in the last ten years in reducing the cost of wheat-raising. Twenty-five millions of dollars a year has been deducted from the previous production cost of the principal crop of Kansas alone. The inventive genius of this manufacturing generation has done that with wheat, for most Kansas farmers use the new implement instead of the old header. Yet there is much talk to the effect that the same procedure cannot be employed in moister climates without injury to the quality of the grain. Possibly so; but the International Harvester Company and other implement manufacturers have offered the windrower and a new principle of harvesting to the Northwest and to Canada. Perhaps the same principle will also serve the Eastern States.

But farms are smaller in the East and their reduced acreage cannot usefully employ the same machinery as the larger farms of the West. Land must be cultivated more intensively, or for that produce which returns a greater profit per unit. It would not serve Cuba to abandon its traditional crop for breadstuffs, even though Java can produce cheaper sugar. It will not serve the Maine farmer to raise wheat any more than his brother of the prairie States can afford to compete with Aroostook County potatoes. The indications of cost study are that the corn-belt farmer would best confine himself to corn and its concomitants, leaving small grains to the dryer districts where land is cheaper. The farmer's problem is one of production and the cost of production.

In this connection, there has been much discussion of what the size of the farm of the future will be. Remembering that the wheat-belt farmer has, with the aid of the tractor and the harvester-thresher, succeeded in completely eliminating the problem of imported harvest labor, it may be suggested that the question of labor, or rather its absence, will solve the matter of area. Where Kansas used to be overrun with laborers who might or might not want to work, the farmer and the members of his family now take care of the cycle of the harvest. He and his tractor can plow, harrow, and drill; or, if he be minded to work long hours, his son can spell him driving the iron horse. When harvest time comes, he himself will

FLEET OF HARVESTER-THRESHERS IN A KANSAS WHEAT-FIELD HARVESTING 640 ACRES A DAY

manipulate the combine, his daughter steers the tractor, and his young son, who is perhaps preparing to go to the State agricultural college in the fall, chugs up in a motor truck to carry the grain away to the elevator or to the bin. If, as some commentators on farm life have stated, this is thought to be a 'lazy' type of farming, try it.... It is work, work for all, old and young, the type of work which in the end must spell either success or be an insolvable equation. It is a kind of work which suggests, because of its efficient economy and freedom from waste, that the proper size farm of the future will be one which, by aid of machinery, a man may operate with no labor except that of himself and his family.

The ultimate in farm equipment has by no means been reached, even with the all-purpose tractor and its attachments. The only thing that can ever limit the introduction of machinery to any task is the interrelation of the overhead charge for equipment and the reduction of the direct labor charge to a minimum. A machine should be asked to demonstrate its ability to pay for itself by the savings it can make. It is, however, true that when there appears a real demand for a mechanical process, in farming or in manufacturing, one will ultimately be supplied. Thus, a successful cotton-picking machine will be at length devised and then there will remain only the relatively simple problem of cotton 'chopping' to solve before the planter can be as free of his labor difficulties as the wheat farmer is to-day. As soon as that happens, he will also be able to complete his crop by machinery, without any labor except that of himself and his family. He will no longer have to provide sustenance for workers who are unproductive for such a large portion of the year. He will be master of his own production.

There will always be some large farms. In certain districts of the world the inhabitants, lowly peasants for the most part, are not of an intelligence to operate a system of the kind I am describing. In other places, climate or soil conditions may dictate a low yield per acre and require such an expanse of territory to make a crop that the limits of family efficiency cannot extend to cover it. Or there may appear some particular genius at organization who can gain more for other men working with and for him than they can earn by themselves. Also some new process of agriculture or of agricultural equipment may be developed to change the face of farming. Dealing, though, with the realm of present knowledge and with those betterments which there is immediate reason to anticipate, it seems to me fair to expect that the size of American farms will for the present continue to be controlled by the extent of the substitution of machinery for labor.

In the broader consideration of the cost of production there appear to be two avenues of progress ahead. Farm operating equipment may be improved and yields may be increased. Far be it from me to urge overproduction as a remedy for the ills of the farm. A business enterprise does not willingly overproduce, and conditions will be better for agriculture if and when it is able to schedule production in terms of estimated future demand. Individual industries have done much in this direction, but they have by no means reached a solution applicable to all industry. As in 1921, each feels that it will survive better than its competitors, and there does not yet exist any industry-wide centralization of the control of total production. There can be no permanent prosperity for factory or farm until this problem is finally solved. Therefore, it is enough to say for the present that, within the limit of the demand, agricultural scientists can do much for farmers by developing better methods of cultivation, soil conservation, fertilization, irrigation, transportation, and control of insects and other pests, to say nothing of a constant study of ordinary day-to-day methods of farm operation. Success depends much more upon the yield per acre than on the number of acres farmed. The American farmer has gone far in per-man efficiency; he has far to go in per-acre efficiency.

The farm equipment industry is very well aware that its future status depends entirely upon the prosperity of the farmer. It has a greater stake in the game than the sale of a certain number of machines built in any one year. Its destiny is mortgaged just as surely as its past has been dedicated. It may grow or it may shrink, but how it develops will be according to how the world deals with the farmer.

International Harvester and the other companies are therefore devoting endless thought and money toward the development of machine methods which will aid in producing the largest possible yield at the lowest possible cost. If there were no other reason, there would be ample justification for the formation of the International Harvester Company in the mechanical processes which its experimental effort has been able to provide. The reaper, the mower, and the binder are the machines upon which implement history is founded. They spelled the initial success of agriculture, and without them the United States could never have become the great farming country that it is. The reaper has gone, but Cyrus Hall McCormick's work is still apparent in the successive machine generations that have arisen from his thought. His first crude implement is now to be interpreted not merely as a page of past history. Its spirit is alive to-day in its heirs —

in the harvester-thresher which is its lineal descendant, in the tractor which is the legitimate offspring of the reaper's substitution of mechanism and power for the puny efforts of an unaided arm, and in the plows and cultivators and legion of machines which are the collateral children of the idea that, in 1831, produced the first farm machine.

Yet our generation must never think that the tale of progress has been told. What does it count in the last analysis if, by means of the most recent machinery combined with a supply of controllable power, the implement companies have found ways and means of increasing the per-man production and reducing the cost accordingly? The farmer has not yet done enough — the companies have not yet done enough. New materials must be found, lighter and cheaper than those with which we now have to deal; unknown methods of reducing wear and increasing the life of machinery must be explored and made practical; undreamed-of methods of manufacturing must be devised to reduce still further the price of equipment; new tools must be invented to reduce time and decrease cost. What if the price of an agricultural implement is less per pound than that of an ordinary cookstove; or if a tractor is relatively less expensive than an automobile, and if its life, measured in terms of the work it does, is longer? Let us immediately begin to try to plan something better. What if gasoline is so cheap that many users of tractors do not bother to use the slightly cheaper kerosene? There are still the interesting possibilities of the combustion qualities of fuel oil to investigate; or there is industrial alcohol which might be made on the farm from vegetable refuse. Or, if imagination be permitted to run further afield into the realm of the 'impossible,' there is wireless transmission of electric power

— controlled lightning — which might some day actuate moving machinery at the wave of a wand.

Such things are chimerical — but they are not one whit more imaginary than were the mechanical visions of Jules Verne or than the tractor was before the reaper was invented. Who will discover them, none knows. Appleby devised the twine binder when McCormick would have given half of his reaper kingdom to have been its discoverer. The International Harvester Company is spending millions on experimental improvements preparing for the future. It will continue to do so as long as the farmer marches on.

Perhaps those certain but now unseen steps ahead in agricultural machine progress will come from the farm itself and not from any of the organized centers of implement research. (Do not forget that the reaper was born on a farm!) The farmer is a very much improved type of mechanic from what he was twenty, thirty, or forty years ago. Many of the old tales of former field experts have to do with fixing a complaining farmer's mental attitude with honeyed words, then banging loudly and innocuously with a hammer on some guiltless piece of iron, and announcing that the job was done. As a matter of fact, it *was* done; for complaints were frequently more fancied than real and were too often due to the operator's own ignorance, of which it would have been tactless to advise him. The advent of the farmer-owned motor car and of the tractor changed that. Out of them farmers got a first grip on the principles of machine operation. Through breakdowns on the road or in the field, far from help, they learned because they had to. Next came the war when perhaps two million farm boys, whether they got to the front or not, were trained by the Government in some mechanical trade or other. They returned home to discover that a tractor was preparing to do the work of the old teams; and with it they were able immediately to put their new knowledge into practice.

A by-product of this mechanical education has been its effect on the quality of farm machinery. While there never has been a time when 'anything would get by,' there is no doubt that former standards of excellence would be considered insufficient to-day. The result of automotive experience and of army trade schools has been that the critical opinion of farmers has advanced as rapidly as the implement companies have been able to improve their product. Thus, the farm equipment operators of the new generation have not only been in a position to demand more of the men who sold them machinery, but, by the same token, have been able to give better attention to the machinery they bought. Where it was once customary for a farmer to call for expert assistance to adjust a knotter-head or the compressor spring on a binder (in all probability he could not have diagnosed the trouble himself, but merely thought that 'the damn thing was rotten and no good'), it is now rare for him to ask for help except in major difficulties. When a machine, whether a tractor or a power-driven disk harrow, has been started by the dealer or the company expert, the farmer usually keeps it in shape himself.

This farmer of to-day is also far better grounded in the science of agriculture than he used to be. The time was when theory was second, but to-day there are thousands of eager students in the agricultural colleges. They are all farm boys and girls, come there to learn the principles of better agriculture. Too many of them go thence to the cities, where it is thought that a college degree is a passport to riches; but many return to their homes and take up the work for which their State has tried to fit them. The 4–H Clubs all over the land are a primary training ground where farm boys and girls may learn better ways of farm usefulness. I think it is safe to say that if the city dweller gave such assiduous attention to the underlying theory of accountancy, banking, and what not as the modern farmer gives to the science of farming, theoretical as well as practical, we should be living in a more efficient world.

The agricultural implement industry of the future is tied inseparably to such men as these. Their duty is to raise those products which feed and clothe the world. Its duty is to serve their need for the tools of their trade. American farming stands in the lead largely because of the native intelligence of American farmers. Here is no peasantry, enslaved for generation after generation to the soil and to exhausting labor. Here is an upstanding man. Why not be glad to serve him? The city is not necessarily opposed to the country just because it manufactures the shoes, clothes, tractors, automobiles, and radios which the country buys; nor does the farmer have to oppose urban interests to sell his produce. In reality we are one community.

Since Cyrus Hall McCormick demanded quality workmanship of his factory because he understood farm needs, the men who have been proud to deal with the reaper and its heirs have regarded their lives as dedicated to a service. I know that Harvester men are happier when they hear that the machine they have made has been sold, and that the metal they have fused with their hope and beaten with the hammer strokes of their existence has been put to work. When they sell it, they are not satisfied until they see it in a field, doing the labor of men who would otherwise be weary and overburdened and serving scantily the world's demand for bread.

Harvester's course is a hundred years old and Harvester men are celebrating the centennial of him who first taught machinery to serve. It is young, for its tradition is strong and forward-looking. Times and conditions, life itself, are changing and the world is demanding new contributions from us, the new servants of its destiny. The age of individualism has passed and the age of collectivism is here. We cannot hope to be pioneers, because the foundation and framework of our economic and social life have already been constructed. We are inheritors in a triumphant succession. But if we cannot build life, we can enhance it: we, too, can learn to serve.

We have problems to meet that are not so new as those of the pioneers, but yet are more complicated. Our forefathers created little enterprises that have grown into huge industries. Our work is so to manage and develop them that they shall continue to march step for step with civilization, never lagging behind in the theory or the practice of producing to meet social needs. Their problem was the production of ideas; our problem is the application of known facts in a broader way. Their task was to conceive; ours is to organize and carry out. If we of to-day are more efficient, it is because we have the benefit of their work; if ours is a wider sphere, it is because we inherit the results of their pioneering; if we build higher, it is because they builded the foundation deep and wide; if we are nearer the ultimate of human happiness, it is because they, the lonely and uplifted pioneers of all our modernity, pierced the age-old barrier and opened the door for us into a limitless field of directed endeavor, of definite achievement, of ordered and organized progress.

THE END

INDEX

INDEX

Accidents to employees, financial relief provided for, 136

Advertising, the beginning of modern, in McCormick's methods, 33, 43–47; broadening of methods of, 99; is now a specialized science, 231

Africa, trade of International Harvester Co. with, 122, 244, 245

Agricultural Extension Department, Harvester Co., 276–79

Agriculture, before the time of McCormick, 4, 5, 13; and industry, 4; in Egypt, 12, 13; in isolated and backward communities of the present day, 14; self-dedication of McCormicks to cause of, 142, 143; European, more provincial than American agriculture, 224; numbers engaged in, 281, 282; the farmer's acquaintance with the science of, 290, 291

All-purpose tractor, 209–12, 219

American Harvester Co., formation of, 107, 108; death of, 108, 109

American manufacturing system, depends upon standardization and mass production, 41

Anderson, Jo, Negro slave, 1, 2, 11

Antipodes, trade of International Harvester Co. with, 122

Appleby, John F., produces twine binder, 70, 71, 92

Argentine, the tractor in, 158; harvester-thresher in, 245

Atkins, Jearum, his 'Iron Man' machine, 64

Auburn Works. See Osborne Works

Aultman-Miller Co., of Akron, Ohio, bought by International Harvester Co., 123, 124

Australia, the tractor in, 158; Harvester service in, 244, 245

Austria, McCormick's reaper in, 56; the tractor in, 158

'Auto buggy,' 124

Automobile industry, discovers that price of labor and labor cost differ, 253, 254

Avery, B. F., of Louisville, 185

Bancroft, Edgar A., 171

Beam, heat-treated, 220

Behel, his idea for the knotter, 71

Bell, worked on problem of reaper, 9, 55

Benefit insurance, 261

Bessemer, Sir Henry, his invention in steel, 3

Binder, wire, 69, 204; twine, 70, 71, 204; steel, 92; 'low-down' corn, 92; right-hander, 93; average yearly sale of, before 1902, 121; compared with harvester-thresher, 213, 214

Binder twine, Deering anticipates McCormick in making, 110; failure of Harvester Co. in, 122, 123, 129, 130; made in Harvester Co.'s Works in Sweden, Germany, and France, 133; sisal fiber for, 176; sale of, 201

'Bindlochine,' 92

Blockmen, 227–29

Branch advertising man, 231

Branch houses, 227; the staff of, 232

Branch manager, the, 227; his force of field experts, 228; his assistant, 230; duties of, 230; is the general agent of the past, 231; has assistance of branch advertising man, 231

Branch warehouses, 233–36

Bread riots, in New York in 1837

British spinners, make first effort at industrialization, 38

330.973
M13 ✓

Property of
Bethany College
Library

23713

330.973
M13

McCormick, Cyrus Hall
The century of the reaper.

330.973	McCormick.
M13	
	The century of the
23713	reaper.

DATE DUE	ISSUED TO
Nov. 8	Nicholas Manuel

DISCARD

Property of
Bethany College
Library